Higher
Chemistry
revision notes

Text copyright © 1999 A. Herd & C. Sparling
Design and layout copyright © 1999 Leckie & Leckie Ltd
Cover image © Tek Image/Science Photo Library

Reprinted 2004

ISBN 1-898890-07-2

Published by
Leckie & Leckie Ltd, 8 Whitehill Terrace, St. Andrews, Scotland, KY16 8RN
tel. 01334 475656   fax. 01334 477392
enquiries@leckieandleckie.co.uk   www.leckieandleckie.co.uk

Special thanks to
Caleb Rutherford (cover design concept), Bruce Ryan (project management),
Hamish Sanderson (illustration), Cathy Sprent (cover design).

Thanks also to Jim MacCallum, Iain McEwen, Ray Mackie and our families

A CIP Catalogue record for this book is available from the British Library.

Leckie & Leckie is a division of Granada Learning Limited, part of ITV plc.

Sandy Herd ✕ Chris Sparling

CHEMISTRY (HIGHER)
A course outline

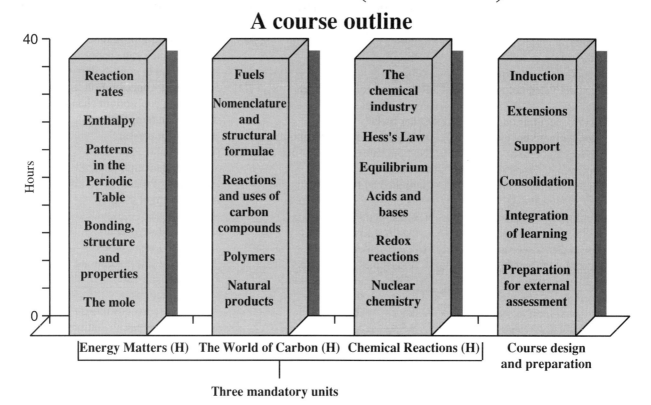

The notes in this publication describe the knowledge and understanding associated with the three mandatory units of your course:

Energy Matters (H)
The World of Carbon (H)
Chemical Reactions (H)

In addition to carrying out regular course practical work to illustrate the course content in these three units, you will also be expected to carry out the **prescribed practical activities** listed below:

- Effect of concentration on the rate of reactions (Unit 1)
- Effect of temperature on the rate of reactions (Unit 1)
- Enthalpy of combustion (Unit 1)
- Oxidation (Unit 2)
- Making esters (Unit 2)
- Factors affecting enzyme activity (Unit 2)
- Hess's Law (Unit 3)
- Quantitative electrolysis (Unit 3)
- Redox titrations (Unit 3)

The chemical points relating to each of these practical activities are also dealt with in these notes.

A brief note from the authors

*Since you will probably have been studying chemistry at either Standard Grade, or at an Intermediate level, you should be aware that this CHEMISTRY(H) course builds on your achievements in **knowledge and understanding**, **problem solving** and **practical skills** from these previous studies. You will see from the sub-topic headings for each unit (column chart above) that many of these will extend and develop areas of chemistry which you will have already encountered. Be sure you have a sound knowledge and understanding of chemistry concepts from these previous courses! In fact, why not get yourself a copy of the best Standard Grade Revision Guide around and begin your preparations for this course!*

We both experienced school chemistry and then worked in chemical industries while continuing our studies to HNC and eventually honours chemistry degree level. As teachers of chemistry for many years, we have maintained our enthusiasm for this - our favourite - subject! We hope that you will enjoy undertaking your chemistry revision from our notes which we have presented in a style and topic order to assist your learning of chemistry. AH & CS

CHEMISTRY(HIGHER) – contents of mandatory course units

UNIT 1   Energy Matters

Reaction rates

You should recall experiments following:

– loss in mass against time and graphs of results!

– gas collected against time and graphs drawn to match the reacting amounts!

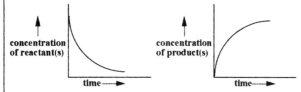

- The rate of chemical reaction may be expressed in terms of the changes in concentration(s) of either reactant(s) or product(s) in unit time.

- The average rate for the initial stages of a reaction is related to $1/t$ (t = time).

$$\text{Average rate} = \frac{\text{change in concentration}}{\text{time}}$$

- The rate units are mol dm^{-3} s^{-1} (moles per cubic decimetre per second) where 1 dm^3 = 1000 cm^3. *Consider this example where the concentration of reactant A is being monitored:*

At start of reaction the concentration of reactant A is 0.6 mol dm^{-3}.

20 seconds into the reaction, only 0.2 mol dm^{-3} of reactant A remains.

$$
\begin{aligned}
\text{Average rate} \atop \text{for this stage} &= \frac{\text{change in concentration}}{\text{time}} \\
&= \frac{(0.6 - 0.2)}{20} \\
&= \frac{0.4}{20} = 0.02 \text{ mol dm}^{-3}\text{ s}^{-1}
\end{aligned}
$$

- The rate of a reaction is fastest at the start and decreases as the reaction proceeds.

- The relative steepness of the graphs is an indication of rate at a particular stage.

- Explosive reactions occur as the result of rapid increases in reaction rate!

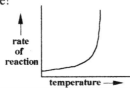

Collision theory

- Collision theory is based on the idea that, before any chemical reaction can take place, the reactant particles must have enough energy to collide together in such a way as to form products.

- Not all collisions between particles – which may be atoms, molecules or ions – result in reaction!

- The minimum kinetic energy required by colliding particles before reaction will occur is known as activation energy (E_A) and this is usually supplied as heat in most chemical reactions.

- In some reactions, light can be used to increase the number of particles with energy greater than E_A.

- Absorption of energy (required to break chemical bonds in reactants is an endothermic process, but energy release, which accompanies the formation of new chemical bonds to create product particles, is an exothermic process.

- The relative energies involved in bond breaking and bond making determine whether a chemical reaction is overall endothermic or exothermic. e.g. the highly exothermic (explosive) H_2/Cl_2 reaction is activated by UV or strong sunlight!

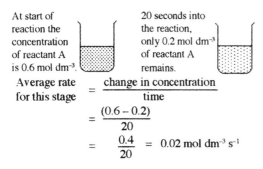

energy absorbed to break bonds (endothermic)	intermediate stage	energy released in forming bonds (exothermic)

- The energy released in an exothermic reaction is the enthalpy change and is represented by $-\Delta H$. *(See page 7 for a fuller treatment of enthalpy.)*

- Because of the need for activation energy (E_A), many exothermic reactions do not occur at easily observable rates e.g. the methane/oxygen(air) explosion is far too fast to be followed in school laboratory rate studies!

- As well as having the necessary activation energy, reactant particles must also be "suitably aligned" for successful collision.

- E_A is the energy required by colliding reactant particles to form the highly energetic, intermediate state called an activated complex.

- It is not essential (or very easy!) to have the exact quantity of each reactant present in reactions and usually one reactant is present in excess.

- Reactants "in excess" can often be calculated. *(See example calculations on page 22.)*

Collision geometry, reaction pathway and activated complex formation

Problems with "explaining" some chemistry can arise because you cannot see what is really happening to the chemical particles during the course of a reaction! It is also quite difficult to explain some theoretical concepts in simple language! Thankfully, diagrams and the use of "model pictures" can help in your descriptions!

Collision geometry

Imagine two diatomic molecules colliding "end-on" i.e.

reactant molecules

This is not the best alignment to form many molecules of the product:

A better collision geometry would be

resulting in the formation of two product particles:

product molecules

Energy changes, reaction pathway and activated complex formation

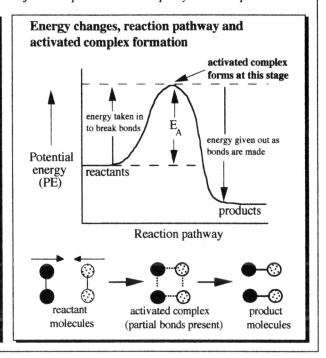

activated complex forms at this stage

energy taken in to break bonds

E_A

energy given out as bonds are made

Potential energy (PE)

reactants

products

Reaction pathway

reactant molecules

activated complex (partial bonds present)

product molecules

The effect of concentration, particle size, temperature and catalyst on rates

CONCENTRATION

Increasing the concentration(s) of reactant(s) causes the rate of collisions between reactant particles to increase.
The number of successful collisions also increases giving rise to an increase in the rate of reaction.

For many reactions, rate is proportional to the concentration(s) of reactant(s).

Rate of reaction / s^{-1}

Concentration / mol dm^{-3}

Average rate values can be obtained from graphs:

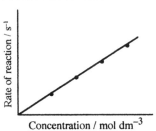

Concentration of reactant A / mol dm^{-3}

Time / s

$$\text{Average rate} = \frac{\text{change in concentration}}{\text{time}}$$

$$= \frac{(1.0 - 0.4)}{20}$$

$$= \frac{0.6}{20} = 0.03 \text{ mol dm}^{-3} \text{ s}^{-1}$$

PARTICLE SIZE

Reducing particle size of solid reactant(s) increases the surface area(s) in contact thus increasing the number of successful collisions between reactant particles. This results in an increase in the rate of reaction.
As particle size of reactant(s) ↓ , surface area(s) ↑

TEMPERATURE

Temperature is a measure of the average kinetic energy of the particles composing a chemical substance.

A small rise in temperature can result in a large increase in reaction rate.

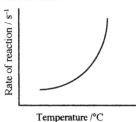

Rate of reaction / s^{-1}

Temperature /°C

For some reactions, an increase of 10°C will approximately double the reaction rate!

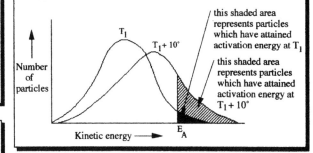

this shaded area represents particles which have attained activation energy at T_1

this shaded area represents particles which have attained activation energy at $T_1 + 10°$

Number of particles

T_1

$T_1 + 10°$

Kinetic energy →

E_A

CATALYSTS

Catalysts speed up reaction rates and reactions are slowed down by inhibitors.
Catalysts provide alternative reaction pathways with lower activation energies.

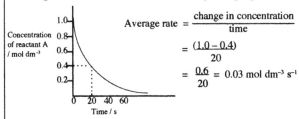

Catalysts

- Increase in reaction rate due to catalyst presence is brought about by the provision of an alternative reaction pathway of lower activation energy.

- This is usually represented graphically:

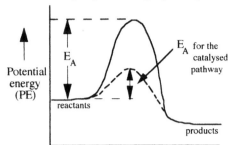

Reaction pathway

- A greater number of reactant particles will now have the necessary lower E_A leading to an increase in the number of successful collisions and a higher rate of reaction.

- Catalysts, which may be solids, liquids or gases, feature in many industrial processes and are not "used up" during reaction.

- Solid catalysts provide "active sites" on their surfaces to which reactant particles are adsorbed.

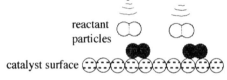

- Particles adsorbed at "active sites" are held in such a way that internal bonds are weakened and the adsorbed reactant(s) can undergo collisions with other reactant particles more readily.

Reaction takes place at the surface–

then product particles leave the "active sites".

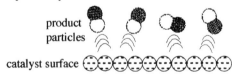

- Catalyst surfaces are said to be poisoned when "active sites" are occupied by reactant impurities e.g. compounds of arsenic poison the vanadium(V) oxide catalyst in the industrial Contact Process.

- Normally, catalysts can undergo regeneration to remove these reactant impurities but, if seriously poisoned, catalysts may require to be renewed.

- Catalytic converters fitted to car exhaust systems convert poisonous NO_x and CO to N_2 and CO_2.

- Pt/Pd/Rh converters in cars have large surface areas (maximising the number of "active sites") and must be used with "lead-free" petrol to avoid poisoning and, thus, reduction in surface activity.

Homogeneous or heterogeneous?

- In homogeneous catalysis, the catalyst has the same physical state as the reactants.
  e.g. pink $Co^{2+}(aq)$ in the laboratory reaction of $H_2O_2(aq)$ with potassium sodium tartrate solution where a green-coloured activated complex forms.

- The catalyst has a different physical state from the reactants in heterogeneous catalysis.
  e.g. solid Fe in the industrial Haber Process for the production of NH_3 from the gases N_2 and H_2.

Enzymes – biological catalysts

- Chemical reactions in animal and plant cells are catalysed by enzymes, which are now used in a number of industrial processes.

- Enzymes are very efficient catalysts, each one being very specific i.e. a particular enzyme catalyses a particular reaction or type of reaction. e.g. invertase converts sucrose to glucose and fructose, and zymase in yeast produces ethanol from fermented carbohydrates.

- Rates of enzyme-controlled reactions are very temperature specific e.g. conversion of sucrose.

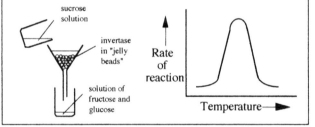

E_A and ΔH from PE diagrams

- Remember, a catalyst lowers activation energy and an inhibitor raises activation energy of a chemical reaction.

- The enthalpy change, $\Delta H = -40$ kJ mol^{-1}, for the reaction below, is not altered by the presence of either a catalyst or an inhibitor.

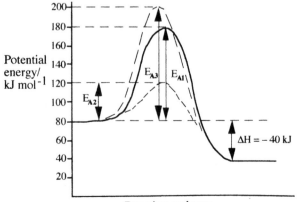

Reaction pathway

- E_{A1} – uncatalysed pathway = 100 kJ mol^{-1}
  E_{A2} – catalysed pathway = 40 kJ mol^{-1}
  E_{A3} – inhibited pathway = 120 kJ mol^{-1}

Enthalpy

- Enthalpy (H) is the heat content or potential energy of a chemical system.

- H_r and H_p are used to denote the total enthalpies of reactants and products, respectively.

- The enthalpy change (ΔH) is the difference in enthalpy between products and reactants.

- $$\boxed{\Delta H = H_p - H_r}$$

- In an exothermic reaction, heat is released from the chemical system to the surroundings.

- In an endothermic reaction, heat is absorbed by the chemical system from the surroundings.

- All chemical reactions can be regarded as having a series of bond breaking and bond making steps. e.g. steps involved in the burning of methane:

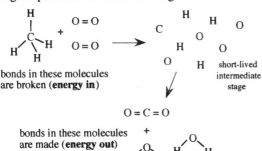

bonds in these molecules are broken (**energy in**)

short-lived intermediate stage

bonds in these molecules are made (**energy out**)

- This overall exothermic reaction and the energy changes involved can be shown diagrammatically:

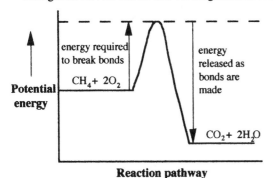

- The difference between the two energy levels for reactants and products is the enthalpy change for the overall reaction.

- If the total energy for bond breaking (as above) is less than the total energy released by the bond making, then the overall reaction is exothermic.

- If the total energy for bond breaking in a reaction is more than the total energy released by the bond making, then the overall reaction is endothermic.

- Where the energy for bond breaking in a reaction balances the energy released by bond making, then the overall reaction is thermoneutral i.e. $\Delta H = 0$.

Exothermic and endothermic potential energy diagrams

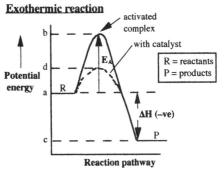

Exothermic reaction

- Activation energy, E_A, is the minimum energy that reactants require before a reaction can take place.

- In an exothermic reaction, $H_p < H_r$.

- The enthalpy change, $\Delta H = H_p - H_r$, has a negative value (enthalpy has been "lost" from the chemical system) i.e. $\Delta H = -$ ve

> **ADVICE FILE**
>
> *"You must be able to express values of the activation energy (E_A) and the enthalpy change (ΔH) in terms of the diagram labels, especially if the axis values are given in terms of a, b, c and d!"*

=> For the uncatalysed exothermic reaction:
  $E_A = b - a$ and $\Delta H = c - a$
and, for the catalysed exothermic reaction:
  $E_A = d - a$ and $\Delta H = c - a$

- Catalysts lower activation energy but have no effect on the enthalpy change for a reaction.

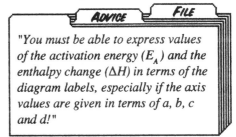

Endothermic reaction

- In an endothermic reaction, $H_p > H_r$.

- The enthalpy change, $\Delta H = H_p - H_r$, has a positive value (enthalpy has been "gained" by the chemical system from the surroundings) i.e. $\Delta H = +$ ve

  => For the uncatalysed endothermic reaction:
    $E_A = b - c$ and $\Delta H = a - c$
  and, for the catalysed endothermic reaction:
    $E_A = d - c$ and $\Delta H = a - c$

- Again, ΔH remains unchanged by the presence of a catalyst which lowers E_A for the reaction.

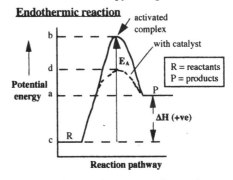

Enthalpy of combustion

- The enthalpy of combustion of a substance is the heat energy released when 1 mol of substance burns completely in excess oxygen.
  e.g. enthalpy of combustion of methane:

$$CH_4 + 2O_2 \longrightarrow CO_2 + 2H_2O \quad \Delta H = -890 \text{ kJ}$$

- Since all combustion reactions are exothermic, the $\Delta H_{combustion}$ values will have a negative sign.

- It is possible to calculate enthalpies of combustion experimentally e.g. for an alkanol series.

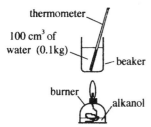

thermometer
100 cm³ of water (0.1kg)
beaker
burner
alkanol

This apparatus with the materials shown could be used in a lab experiment but the apparatus would normally be surrounded by a draught shield with the beaker supported on a tripod stand using a clay pipe or silicate triangle in place of the wire gauze.

- Even this experimental set up would not give very accurate results because of great heat loss to the surroundings and the incomplete combustion of the alkanol in air (~ 20% oxygen).

- The heat released from the combustion of the alkanol is used to heat up the mass of water.

- This amount of heat can be calculated using the expression:
  $$H = c\,m\,\Delta T$$
  where H = heat gained by the water (kJ),
  c = specific heat capacity of water ($4.18 \text{ kJ kg}^{-1} \text{ K}^{-1}$),
  m = mass of water (kg)
  and, ΔT = the change in temperature (K)
  ΔH (in kJ mol^{-1}) is calculated from this data.

ADVICE FILE

" If you are a non-physics student, this will be the first time that you will have met the very important $H = cm\Delta T$ equation! It is also used to calculate enthalpy changes in endothermic reactions when heat is taken from the surroundings into the chemical system."

- Exothermic reactions carried out in laboratory experiments result in a rise in temperature of the materials and the calculated ΔH will be negative.

- Endothermic reactions carried out in laboratory experiments result in a fall in temperature of the materials and the calculated ΔH will be positive.

Advice on enthalpy calculations

Data Booklets list enthalpies of reaction in kJ mol^{-1} but frequently you will be writing equations using amounts other than 1 mol and so kJ mol^{-1} units would not be appropriate! So, always use kJ units to match the quantities in your written equations! Also, pay attention to the use of state symbols (s), (l) and (g) in your equations and remember to change the sign when reversing an equation!

i.e.
$$C(s) + O_2(g) \longrightarrow CO_2(g) \quad \Delta H = -394 \text{ kJ}$$
$$2C(s) + 2O_2(g) \longrightarrow 2CO_2(g) \quad \Delta H = -788 \text{ kJ}$$
$$2CO_2(g) \longrightarrow 2C(s) + 2O_2(g) \quad \Delta H = +788 \text{ kJ}$$

ΔH of combustion calculations

When 1 g of ethanol is completely burned, the temperature of 500 cm³ of water is raised from 20 °C to 34 °C.
Calculate the enthalpy of combustion of ethanol.

Remember, (a) $1C° = 1K$
(b) *m = mass of water used!*
(c) *1 cm³ water has a mass of 1 g*

1 mol of ethanol, $C_2H_5OH = 46$ g
$c_{water} = 4.18 \text{ kJ kg}^{-1} \text{ K}^{-1}$
$m = 500 \text{ g} = 0.5 \text{ kg}$
$\Delta T = (34 - 20) = 14 \text{ C}°$ or 14 K

Applying $H = c\,m\,\Delta T$
$H = 4.18 \times 0.5 \times 14 \text{ kJ}$
$H = 29.26 \text{ kJ}$
=> 1 g ethanol burned to release 29.26 kJ
=> 46 g ethanol burned to release 29.26×46 kJ
$= 1346 \text{ kJ}$
=> $\Delta H_{combustion}$ ethanol $= -1346 \text{ kJ mol}^{-1}$

When 110 cm³ of methane was burned, it heated 100 cm³ of water from 20 °C to 30 °C.
Calculate ΔH of combustion for methane.
(Molar volume of methane = 22.5 dm³ mol^{-1})

Remember, (a) $1C° = 1K$
(b) *m = mass of water used!*
(c) *1 cm³ water has a mass of 1 g*

$c = 4.18 \text{ kJ kg}^{-1} \text{ K}^{-1}$
$m = 100 \text{ g} = 0.1 \text{ kg}$
$\Delta T = (30 - 20) = 10 \text{ C}°$ or 10 K

Applying $H = c\,m\,\Delta T$
$= 4.18 \times 0.1 \times 10 \text{ kJ}$
$= 4.18 \text{ kJ}$
=> 110 cm³ gas burned to release 4.18 kJ
=> 22500 cm³ gas would release $\dfrac{4.18 \times 22500}{110}$ kJ
$= 855 \text{ kJ}$
=> $\Delta H_{combustion}$ methane $= -855 \text{ kJ mol}^{-1}$

Enthalpy of solution (ionic solid)

When ionic compounds dissolve in water, heat energy may be absorbed or given out!

- The enthalpy of solution of an ionic substance is the enthalpy change when 1 mol of the substance is dissolved completely in water. (ΔH values may be + ve or – ve.)

$$Na^+Cl^-(s) + aq \longrightarrow Na^+(aq) + Cl^-(aq) \qquad \Delta H = +5 \text{ kJ}$$

$$Ca^{2+}(NO_3^-)_2(s) + aq \rightarrow Ca^{2+}(aq) + 2NO_3^-(aq) \quad \Delta H = -19 \text{ kJ}$$

What processes determine whether dissolving is an overall endothermic or exothermic process?

- Lattice-breaking enthalpy is the change in enthalpy when 1 mol of a solid ionic compound is dissociated into its constituent ions in the gaseous state. (ΔH is always + ve.)

$$NaCl(s) \longrightarrow Na^+(g) + Cl^-(g) \qquad \Delta H = + 776 \text{ kJ}$$

- Enthalpy of hydration is the enthalpy change when 1 mol of gaseous ions completely hydrates in water.

$$Na^+(g) + aq \longrightarrow Na^+(aq) \qquad \Delta H = - 390 \text{ kJ}$$
$$Cl^-(g) + aq \longrightarrow Cl^-(aq) \qquad \Delta H = - 381 \text{ kJ}$$
(ΔH is always – ve.)

Try to consider the solution of NaCl(s) in two stages:

(1) Separation of the ionic compound into gaseous ions by absorbing lattice-breaking enthalpy.

$$NaCl(s) \longrightarrow Na^+(g) + Cl^-(g) \qquad \Delta H = + 776 \text{ kJ}$$

(2) Hydration of the gaseous ions by water molecules to release enthalpy of hydration.

$$Na^+(g) + Cl^-(g) \rightarrow Na^+(aq) + Cl^-(aq) \quad \Delta H = -771 \text{ kJ}$$

- The overall enthalpy of solution is the sum of the lattice-breaking enthalpy and the hydration enthalpies *.

$$\Delta H_{solution} = \Delta H_{lattice\text{-}breaking} + \Delta H_{hydration}$$

$$* \; Na^+(g) + aq \longrightarrow Na^+(aq), \qquad \Delta H = - 390 \text{ kJ}$$
$$Cl^-(g) + aq \longrightarrow Cl^-(aq) \qquad \Delta H = - 381 \text{ kJ}$$

Can you see that the hydration enthalpies of ionic compounds can be obtained by adding together the hydration enthalpies of their component ions?

- For the solution process of an ionic compound (general case):

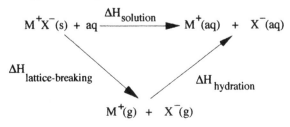

Can you see now that the exothermic solution of $Ca(NO_3)_2$ is due to $\Delta H_{lattice\text{-}breaking} < \Delta H_{hydration}$?

ΔH solution calculation

When 1 g sodium hydroxide is dissolved completely in 50 cm³ water, the temperature rises by 5 K. Calculate ΔH of solution for sodium hydroxide.

$$\text{Mass of 1 mol NaOH} = 23 + 16 + 1$$
$$= 40 \text{ g}$$

$$H = c \, m \, \Delta T \text{ (Note that the solution } \sim \text{ water for c and m)}$$
$$= 4.18 \times 0.05 \times 5 \text{ kJ}$$
$$= 1.045 \text{ kJ for dissolving 1 g}$$
$$\Rightarrow \Delta H_{solution} = - 1.045 \times 40 \text{ kJ mol}^{-1}$$
$$= - 41.8 \text{ kJ mol}^{-1}$$

Trends in hydration enthalpies

- Gaseous metal ions show trends in enthalpies of hydration which relate to ion size, charge and thus ability to attract H_2O molecules.

$$Li^+(g) \longrightarrow Li^+(aq) \qquad \Delta H = -499 \text{ kJ}$$
$$Na^+(g) \longrightarrow Na^+(aq) \qquad \Delta H = -390 \text{ kJ}$$
$$K^+(g) \longrightarrow K^+(aq) \qquad \Delta H = -305 \text{ kJ}$$
(Ion size increases down Group 1.)

$$Na^+(g) \longrightarrow Na^+(aq) \qquad \Delta H = - 390 \text{ kJ}$$
$$Mg^{2+}(g) \longrightarrow Mg^{2+}(aq) \qquad \Delta H = -1891 \text{ kJ}$$
$$Al^{3+}(g) \longrightarrow Al^{3+}(aq) \qquad \Delta H = -4613 \text{ kJ}$$
(Ion size decreases across period but main effect is due to increasing ion charge.)

- Gaseous negative ions also display trends in hydration enthalpies.

  Can you see how hydration enthalpy is affected by change in ion size?

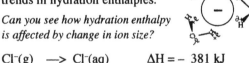

$$Cl^-(g) \longrightarrow Cl^-(aq) \qquad \Delta H = - 381 \text{ kJ}$$
$$Br^-(g) \longrightarrow Br^-(aq) \qquad \Delta H = - 351 \text{ kJ}$$
$$I^-(g) \longrightarrow I^-(aq) \qquad \Delta H = - 307 \text{ kJ}$$

Enthalpy of neutralisation

- Enthalpy of neutralisation is the enthalpy change when 1 mol of water molecules is formed in an acid/base neutralisation reaction.
  i.e.

$$H^+(aq) + OH^-(aq) \longrightarrow H_2O(l) \qquad \Delta H = - 57 \text{ kJ}$$
(ΔH is always – ve.)

When 50 cm³ 1 mol dm⁻³ HCl(aq) is added to 50 cm³ 1 mol dm⁻³ NaOH(aq), the temperature rises by 6.5 °C. Calculate ΔH of neutralisation for this reaction.

Mols of acid (H^+) = conc. × vol. = 1 × 0.05 = 0.05
Mols of alkali (OH^-) = conc. × vol. = 1 × 0.05 = 0.05
Mass of solution = (50 + 50) g = 100 g = 0.1 kg

$$
\begin{array}{lllll}
 & H^+(aq) & + \; OH^-(aq) & \longrightarrow & H_2O(l) \\
 & 1 \text{ mol} & 1 \text{ mol} & \longrightarrow & 1 \text{ mol} \\
\Rightarrow & 0.05 \text{ mol} & 0.05 \text{ mol} & \longrightarrow & 0.05 \text{ mol}
\end{array}
$$

$$H = c \, m \, \Delta T \text{ (Note that salt solution } \sim \text{ water for c and m)}$$
$$= 4.18 \times 0.1 \times 6.5 \text{ kJ}$$
$$= 2.72 \text{ kJ for 0.05 mol } H_2O \text{ formed}$$
$$\Rightarrow \Delta H_{neutralisation} = - 2.72 \times 20 = - 54.4 \text{ kJ mol}^{-1}$$

Patterns in the Periodic Table

- The modern Table was developed from the pioneering work of Mendeleev who placed known elements in groups and periods on the basis of increasing atomic mass and known similarities in chemical behaviour.

- Mendeleev left gaps in his early Periodic Table for elements still to be "discovered".

- Trends (patterns) in element properties within groups and periods relate to bonding and structure.

Bonding, structure and properties

Noble gases – discrete atoms

- Noble gases, form Group 0 of the Periodic Table, and are monatomic gases with full outermost electron shells.

Noble gas	Symbol	Electron arrangement
helium	He	2
neon	Ne	2, 8
argon	Ar	2, 8, 8
krypton	Kr	2, 8, 18, 8
xenon	Xe	2, 8, 18, 18, 8
radon	Rn	2, 8, 18, 32, 18, 8

- Chemical stability and unreactivity of noble gases is related to full outer shell electron arrangements.

- A trend in the very low melting points of the noble gases indicates the presence of very weak van der Waals' forces between atoms which increase in strength going down this Group.

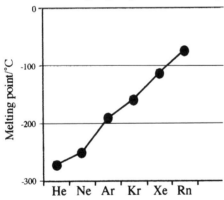

- Van der Waals' forces arise from electrostatic attractions between temporary dipoles and induced dipoles resulting from electrons moving position in atoms (and molecules).

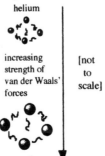

	Electrons per atom	
He	2	
Ne	10	
Ar	18	increasing strength of van der Waals' forces
Kr	36	[not to scale]
Xe	54	
Rn	86	

- Van der Waals' forces are much weaker than all other types of chemical bonding.

Halogens – discrete molecules

- In such covalent bonds, identical atoms are held together by electrostatic forces of attraction between positively charged nuclei and negatively charged shared electrons.

- The halogens ("salt formers") or Group 7 elements of the Periodic Table have seven electrons in the outer shells of their atoms which combine readily to form discrete, diatomic covalent molecules.
  e.g. chlorine

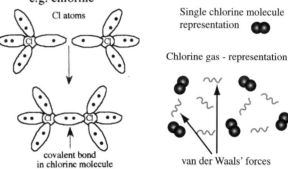

Cl atoms

Single chlorine molecule representation

Chlorine gas - representation

covalent bond in chlorine molecule

van der Waals' forces

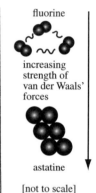

fluorine

increasing strength of van der Waals' forces

astatine

[not to scale]

	Electrons per molecule	Physical state
F_2	18	gas
Cl_2	34	gas
Br_2	70	liquid
I_2	106	solid
At_2	170	solid

- The trend in physical state going down Group 7 is due to increasing molecular mass and the strength of van der Waals' forces which increase due to greater numbers of electrons per molecule.

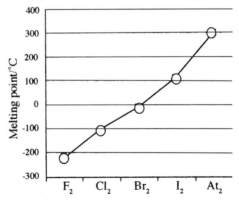

- Intramolecular covalent bonds within halogen molecules are strong, while the intermolecular van der Waals' forces are relatively weak.

- Summary:
  Discrete covalent molecular gases – F_2 and Cl_2
  Discrete covalent molecular liquid – Br_2
  Discrete covalent molecular solids – I_2 and At_2

Covalent molecular elements

- Group 5

  Discrete covalent molecular gas – N_2 $N\equiv N$

  Discrete covalent molecular solid – P_4

- Group 6

  Discrete covalent molecular gas – O_2 $O=O$

  Discrete covalent molecular solid – S_8

- Molecular forms of carbon (Group 4) were discovered in 1985 from soot prepared from graphite vapour.

- Many even-numbered, ball-shaped, carbon clusters (fullerenes) were found, C_{60} being quite stable.

- The molecular shape of C_{60} (buckminsterfullerene) resembles a modern football and is made of C_6 "rings" bonded to C_5 "rings"!

- As fullerenes appear to have some useful properties e.g. C_{60} is a magnetic and almost frictionless solid, they are being researched vigorously for new applications!

Covalent network elements

- The atoms of some elements in Group 3 and Group 4 of the Periodic Table are bonded in covalent networks or large lattice structures.

- Boron exists as B_{12} units linked together. The very high m.p. of 2300 °C reflects the strength of the covalent bonds.

  A single B_{12} unit

- Carbon exists mainly as two high melting point covalent network solids – diamond and graphite. (Different crystalline forms of the same element are called polymorphs or allotropes.)

- Properties of the diamond form of carbon
  - Very high m.p.
  - Regular tetrahedral arrangement.
  - All four outer electrons of each carbon atom involved in strong covalent bonding.
  - Non-conductor of electricity.
  - Extremely hard substance.
  - Used for cutting and as a precious jewel.

- Properties of the graphite form of carbon
  - Very high m.p.
  - Layered structure of atoms in hexagonal plates.
  - Three of the four outer electrons of each carbon atom involved in strong covalent bonding within the hexagonal layers.
  - The fourth outer electron on each atom is free to move within the hexagonal layers.
  - These electron movements within layers create the weak Van der Waals' forces between layers.
  - Conductor of electricity.
  - Soft, greasy/slippery feel to touch.
  - Used as lubricating material and pencil "lead".

Networks at work!

- Silicon – in Group 4 – has a covalent network structure similar to diamond.

- Unlike diamond, however, silicon can conduct electricity very poorly i.e. it is classified as a semiconductor or metalloid.

- Silicon, Si, and germanium, Ge, are much better conductors of electricity when they are "doped" with impurities and they are used widely to make chips for computers.

Metallic lattices

- Most of the elements are metals occurring essentially in Groups 1, 2 and 3 and in both transition series of chemical elements.

  (Note: Group 4 elements Sn and Pb are metals.)

- The outer electron(s) of each metal atom can move freely within a closely packed metallic lattice.

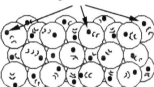

fast-moving outer shell electrons

part of a metallic lattice

Electrostatic attraction between a lattice of positively charged ions and loosely-held outer shell electrons is called metallic bonding.

- General properties of metallic elements
  - Mainly shiny solids. (Hg is the only liquid metal at normal temperature.)
  - Conduct electricity when solid or when molten.
  - Do not change chemically while conducting electricity.

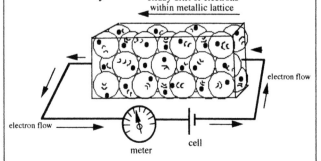

steady drift of electrons within metallic lattice

electron flow

electron flow

meter

cell

  - Melting points are fairly high (except Group 1).
  - Of major use in the production of electrical components.
  - Mixtures of metals are called alloys. (Properties of individual metallic elements are changed by alloying with other elements.)
  - Most metals are insoluble.

Bonding and structure of the elements (H – Ca)

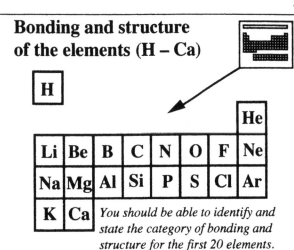

You should be able to identify and state the category of bonding and structure for the first 20 elements.

- **Monatomic gases**
  The only bonding present is van der Waals' forces between atoms.

- **Discrete covalent molecular diatomic gases**
  Strong intramolecular covalent bonding with van der Waals' forces between individual molecules.

- **Discrete covalent molecular solids**
  Strong intramolecular covalent bonding with van der Waals' forces between the molecular units.

  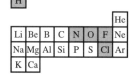

  P_4 – linked tetrahedrons
  S_8 – puckered, crown-like rings

- **Covalent network solids**
  Very strong internal covalent bonding within large lattice structures.

- **Metallic lattices**
  Fairly strong metallic bonds generally but weaker for Group 1 "Alkali Metals".

  Lithium, sodium and potassium metals have their atoms arranged in the structure often simply referred to as b.c.c.

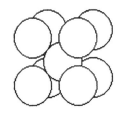

body centred cubic packing

Physical properties of the elements (H – Ca)

NB. Information may differ between Data Booklets.

You are expected to be able to draw and/or to interpret graphs and charts of data on physical properties of the elements.

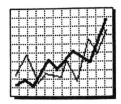

- Many physical properties exhibit general trends * either from left to right across a period or from top to bottom down a group in the Periodic Table.

  * Some values in properties show fluctuations from the general trend which require a more advanced explanation beyond this level of chemistry.

Sizes of atoms of the elements

There are obvious problems in producing a "scale of atom size" because this depends on how an atom bonds to other atoms! Some atoms do not bond with other atoms! However, in spite of such difficulties, chemists have given covalent radii values to elements.

- The covalent radius of an element is half the distance between the nuclei of two of its bonded atoms.

The distance between the arrow heads is the covalent radius.

TRENDS

- Atom size increases due to extra electron shells being present.

- Outer electrons are shielded from increasing nuclear charge attraction ("screening effect").

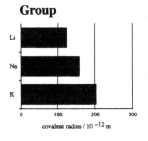

Group

- Atom size decreases due to the increasing nuclear charge attraction on the electron shells.

- As electron shells are pulled in, contraction of atom size occurs across the period.

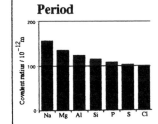

Period

Densities of elements

- The mass per unit volume of an element not only depends on the mass of individual atoms but on the packing arrangement of the atoms in the element structure.

- The different strengths of bonding types in the element structures determine the closeness or the openness of atom packing and thus controls the densities of elements.

TRENDS

Group

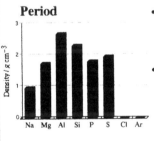

Density / kg m⁻³

- A general increase in density down the group of noble gases due to the increasing atomic mass and increasing van der Waals' forces.

- Not all groups in the Periodic Table show such a steady trend in densities although there is a general increase downwards.

Period

Density / g cm⁻³

Na Mg Al Si P S Cl Ar

- A general increase in density from Na —> Mg —> Al due to increased metallic bonding.

- The covalent network nature of Si leads to a higher than expected density over P and S which exist as dense P_4 and S_8 units but these are held together by weak van der Waals' forces.

- Chlorine (diatomic) and argon (monatomic) exist as gases held together by weak van der Waals' forces at normal temperature and pressure and thus they have very low densities.

Defining ionisation energies

- The first ionisation energy of an element is the energy required to remove one electron from each atom in a mole of atoms in the gaseous state.

e.g. $Li(g) \longrightarrow Li^+(g) + e^-$ $\Delta H = +526 \, kJ$
       $Mg(g) \longrightarrow Mg^+(g) + e^-$ $\Delta H = +744 \, kJ$

- Successive ionisation energies of elements are defined as and represented in a similar manner to the first ionisation energies.

e.g. The second ionisation energy of lithium
       $Li^+(g) \longrightarrow Li^{2+}(g) + e^-$ $\Delta H = +7300 \, kJ$
The second ionisation energy of magnesium
       $Mg^+(g) \longrightarrow Mg^{2+}(g) + e^-$ $\Delta H = +1450 \, kJ$
The third ionisation energy of lithium
       $Li^{2+}(g) \longrightarrow Li^{3+}(g) + e^-$ $\Delta H = +11800 \, kJ$

Ionisation energies of elements

TRENDS

First ionisation energies

- There is a decrease in these values down any group as the outer electrons of atoms become further away from the nucleus and thus easier to remove.

- Atom size increases down the groups due to successive additions of full electron shells which effectively shield outer electrons from the nuclear charge attraction in spite of this increasing down any group.

Group

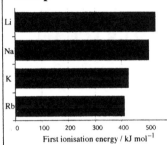

First ionisation energy / kJ mol⁻¹

Period

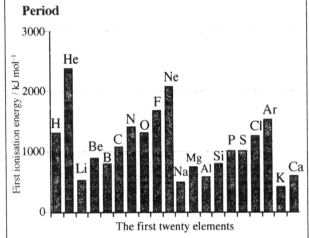

Study the bar chart above and identify the first three periods i.e. H —> He; Li —> Ne and Na —> Ar.
Can you see that the values increase generally across each period?

- Across any period, electrons are gradually being added to atoms in the same electron shell.

- However, at the same time as electrons are being added, protons (and some neutrons) are also being added to the nuclei of the atoms.

- The increasing nuclear charge attraction across a period, pulls in electron shells closer to the nucleus making it more difficult (more energy is required) to remove outer electrons from atoms.

- The very high, first ionisation energies for the noble gases relates to the great chemical stability of a full outer shell of electrons.

- Ions which have the same electron arrangement (isoelectronic) as the noble gases also have very high ionisation energies.

e.g. The second ionisation energy of lithium

       $Li^+(g) \longrightarrow Li^{2+}(g) + e^-$ $\Delta H = +7300 \, kJ$
isoelectronic
with helium

Metallic character

- Elements which are shiny, malleable, ductile and good conductors of heat and electricity possess metallic character.

- Metallic character is due to the presence of very mobile electrons within a structure.

- Restriction of movement of such mobile electrons within a structure lowers the degree of metallic character.

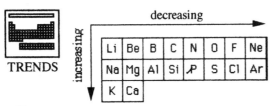

TRENDS

Group

- Metallic character increases down a group due to the increasing mobility of outer shell electrons which are more loosely held as the atom size increases and these electrons become increasingly shielded from the nuclear charge attraction.

  You should now appreciate why metals Sn and Pb appear near the bottom of Group 4!

Period

- Metallic character decreases across a period.

- The increasing nuclear charge attraction for the outer electrons lowers their mobility and thus their availability to take part in metallic bonding.

- The trend is metals -> metalloids -> non-metals.

- Metalloids display metallic and non-metallic characteristics e.g. Si, Ge, As, Sb.

Melting and boiling

- Melting is the change of state – solid to liquid.

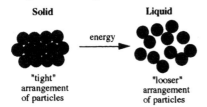

- Boiling is the change of state – liquid to gas.

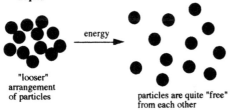

Melting/boiling points of elements

- Comparing melting points and boiling points of elements provides some information on relative strengths of the bonding types within element structures.

- High melting points and high boiling points relate to strong attractive forces being overcome to bring about the appropriate change of state.

TRENDS

You must be careful when describing group trends since these depend on the type of bonding within the elements.

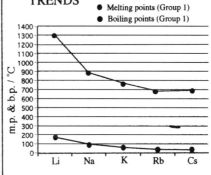

- There is a general decrease in the strength of the metallic bonding from Li –> Cs.

- The lattice of Li^+ ions in lithium metal is most tightly bonded by the "sea" of mobile electrons.

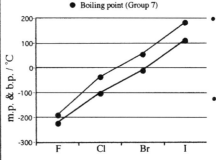

- Iodine molecules are more strongly bonded together than those of the gas fluorine.

- The trend is due to increasing molecular mass and strength of van der Waals' forces.

Can you see similarities in the melting point and boiling point trends for the period Na –> Ar ?

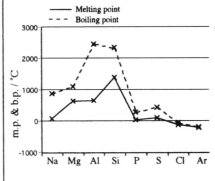

- A general rise in melting point from Na –> Al is due to the increase in strength of the metallic bonds.

- The high melting point of Si reflects the strong bonds in the covalent network.

- The sudden fall to lower values in Groups 5 and 6 is due to the fact that P_4 and S_8 molecules are held together by weak van der Waals' forces which are broken – not the intramolecular covalent bonds – during the changes of state.

- Van der Waals' forces are weak between Cl_2 molecules and even weaker forces hold Ar atoms together.

Non-polar and polar bonding

ADVICE **FILE**

" Since the stable atoms of the noble gases do not bond * generally to atoms of other elements, the periodic trends discussed will only feature Group 1 to Group 7."

* A few noble gas compounds do exist.

e.g. $XePtF_6$, XeO_3, XeF_2, XeF_4, KrF_2.

- Atoms of different elements have different attractions (electronegativities) for bonding electrons.

TRENDS

H   **increasing electronegativity**
i.e. increasing attraction for bonding electrons

decreasing electronegativity
i.e. decreasing attraction for bonding electrons

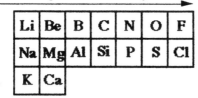

Li	Be	B	C	N	O	F
Na	Mg	Al	Si	P	S	Cl
K	Ca					

- Overlapping of half-filled electron clouds from identical non-metals atoms (no electronegativity difference) produces equal sharing of the bonding electrons i.e. pure non-polar covalent bonding.
e.g. hydrogen, H_2

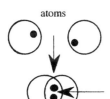

atoms

molecule

The two hydrogen nuclei are held together by their common attraction for the shared pair of electrons.

covalent bond – the **link** holding atoms together in a molecule.

- F_2 and Cl_2 have non-polar covalent bonding with one pair of bonding electrons being equally shared.
i.e.   F – F   and   Cl – Cl

- O_2 and N_2 have non-polar covalent bonding but with two pairs and three pairs of bonding electrons respectively being equally shared.
i.e.   O = O   and   N≡N

- In the majority of covalent compounds the bonding electrons are not shared equally between bonded atoms but are attracted more towards one of the atoms (more electronegative) resulting in polar-covalent bonding.
e.g. hydrogen fluoride, HF

$$F_{EN} > H_{EN}$$
[EN = electronegativity]

$$\overset{\partial+}{H} - \overset{\partial-}{F}$$

The signs placed above the atoms show the **polarity** of the bond.

$\partial+$ = slight positive charge
$\partial-$ = slight negative charge

Polar bonds and polar molecules

ADVICE **FILE**

" OK – so up until now you have been following the notes on chemical bonding but we suspect you might be ready to switch off at the appearance of the $\partial+$ and the $\partial-$! Don't panic! Just read on slowly and come to grips with this very important part of the bonding topic!"

- The polarity of a covalent bond depends on the different electronegativities of the bonded atoms.

$$\overset{\partial-}{C}\overset{\partial+}{-H} \quad \overset{\partial-}{N}\overset{\partial+}{-H} \quad \overset{\partial-}{O}\overset{\partial+}{-H} \quad \overset{\partial-}{F}\overset{\partial+}{-H}$$

[Remember the atom with the greater share of the bonding electrons has the $\partial-$ charge.]

- Molecules described as polar have a permanent dipole which results in additional intermolecular attractions.

Confused? We hope not! Please read on!

- A non-polar molecule may contain polar bonds which are symmetrically opposed.

The four polar bonds are arranged symmetrically in space i.e. they "cancel" each other out.

CH_4 is a non-polar molecule.

$$\overset{\partial-}{O}=\overset{\partial+}{C}=\overset{\partial-}{O}$$

The polar bonds are arranged symmetrically in this linear molecule i.e. they "cancel" each other out.

CO_2 is a non-polar molecule.

- A polar molecule contains polar bonds which are not symmetrically opposed.

The angular shape of the water molecule gives an uneven charge distribution. The two polar bonds do not "cancel" each other out.

H_2O is a polar molecule.

- Polar liquids may be distinguished from non-polar liquids using a charged plastic rod brought near a fine jet of liquid falling from a burette.
The uneven charge distribution in molecules of the liquid B interacts with the charged plastic rod and deflects the stream.

Liquid A   Liquid B

charged rods

Liquid B is polar.

Structures and properties – polar and non-polar molecules

- The $\partial+$ and $\partial-$ sites on polar molecules bring about additional intermolecular attractions over and above expected van der Waals' forces from the number of electrons per molecule.

- Evidence for such additional intermolecular attractions is apparent in comparisons of melting and boiling points of non-polar and polar liquids with similar molecular mass.

e.g.

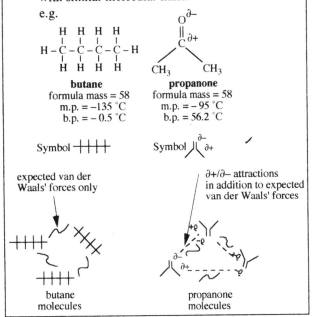

butane
formula mass = 58
m.p. = –135 °C
b.p. = – 0.5 °C

propanone
formula mass = 58
m.p. = – 95 °C
b.p. = 56.2 °C

Symbol ++++

Symbol

expected van der Waals' forces only

$\partial+/\partial-$ attractions in addition to expected van der Waals' forces

butane molecules

propanone molecules

Hydrogen bonding

- Other intermolecular attractions are found in compounds containing hydrogen atoms bonded to atoms of highly electronegative elements such as oxygen, nitrogen and fluorine.

- They are called hydrogen bonds and they are slightly stronger than van der Waals' forces.

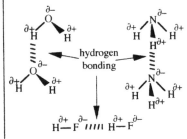

The hydrogen bonds are formed between hydrogen atoms on one molecule to the atoms of oxygen or nitrogen or fluorine on other molecules.

- Hydrogen bonding is also present in alkanols and amines. The important $N–H^{\partial+}$ ///// $^{\partial-}N$ hydrogen bonds enable complex proteins and nucleic acids to be synthesised in cells.

- The higher than expected boiling points of the hydrides NH_3 and HF, in relation to the trends within their respective groups, is attributable to intermolecular hydrogen bonding present.

- Dimers and trimers of highly polar molecules can form giving rise to higher than expected molecular masses e.g. molecular mass units of 20, 40 and 60 corresponding to HF, $(HF)_2$ and $(HF)_3$ are known.

Hydrogen bonding in water

- Hydrogen bonding in water accounts for:

(a) its higher than expected b.p. for its relatively low molecular mass.

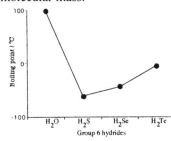

Similar trends or patterns are obtained for the Group 5 and Group 7 hydrides.

(b) its viscosity, which is high when compared with liquids of even higher molecular mass.

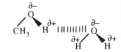

water
formula mass = 18

is more viscous (less runny) than

dimethyl ether
formula mass = 46

(c) its miscibility with low molecular mass alkanols.

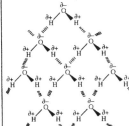

Ethanol and propanol are also completely miscible with water but higher alkanols display decreasing solubilty trends.

(d) the formation of ice on the surface of freezing water. (Water has its maximum density at 4 °C.)

On cooling below 4 °C, H_2O molecules begin to arrange themselves into an open lattice formation held in place by hydrogen bonds. The less dense, ice crystals formed float to the surface.

Solubility in non-polar solvents

- In general terms, non-polar substances are much more soluble in non-polar solvents e.g. toluene, 1,1,1-trichloroethane and petroleum spirit.

- Iodine, $I_2(s)$, is soluble in 1,1,1-trichloroethane as there is sufficient energy released on interaction of these molecules to overcome weak van der Waals' forces and to permit the solution process.

solvent molecules

solution of I_2 in 1,1,1-trichloroethane

- Candle wax, oils and other substances with high carbon/hydrogen content also readily dissolve in non-polar solvents.

- Non-polar solvent molecules can form only very weak attractions to either ionic or polar solutes and release only small amounts of energy which is insufficient to break bonds in these substances and to bring about the solution process.

Solubility in polar solvents

- In general terms, ionic substances are soluble in polar solvents e.g. water and ethanol.

(a) The $\partial+$ and $\partial-$ charges on the solvent molecules are attracted to the + ve and − ve ions in an ionic lattice releasing energy (energy of hydration).

(b) This energy begins to break the ionic bonds in the ionic lattice i.e. lattice energy is absorbed.

(c) In turn, more + ve and − ve ions released become hydrated (energy given out) and so the solution process evolves.

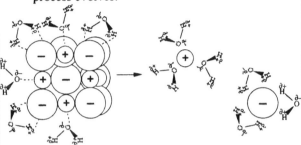

e.g. $Na^+Cl^-(s) + aq \longrightarrow Na^+(aq) + Cl^-(aq)$

- Some polar molecules ionise in polar solvents. e.g. HCl(g) in water.

[not to scale]

Energy released when attractions take place (as shown) more than compensates for energy required to break the polar-covalent bonds in the hydrogen chloride molecules.

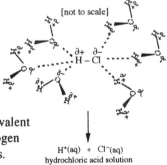

$H^+(aq) + Cl^-(aq)$
hydrochloric acid solution

- Generally, polar solvents do not dissolve non-polar solutes e.g. iodine, $I_2(s)$, is not very soluble in water.

Lattices and covalent bonding

- Silicon carbide, SiC, is a high m.p. covalent network with a diamond lattice crystal structure which is very difficult to break down since this involves breaking very strong covalent bonds.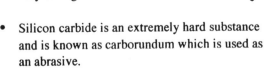

- Silicon carbide is an extremely hard substance and is known as carborundum which is used as an abrasive.

- Silicon dioxide, SiO_2, is another high m.p. compound with a giant network lattice structure similar to diamond and containing very strong covalent Si – O – Si bonds. Silicon dioxide is also known as silica.

Lattices and ionic bonding

- Compounds made from atoms with very different electronegativities are more likely to be composed of ions of opposite charge formed as a result of electron transfer from a metal to a non-metal atom. e.g. potassium fluoride, KF.

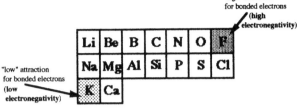

"high" attraction for bonded electrons (high electronegativity)

"low" attraction for bonded electrons (low electronegativity)

	K	F
Reacting elements	K	F
Electron arrangements	2, 8, 8, **1**	2, **7**
During reaction	loses $1e^-$	gains $1e^-$
	transfer of an electron	
Resulting in the electron arrangements	2, 8, **8**	2, **8**
Formation of ions	K^+	F^-

There is electrostatic attraction between the oppositely charged ions.

K^+F^-

The force of attraction between ions is called the ionic bond.

[Not to scale]

Ions are "locked" together in the lattice and cannot move about to conduct electricity.

Solid ionic compounds do not conduct electricity.

- Ionic compounds e.g. fluorides and chlorides, can normally be made by direct combination of elements.

  e.g. $2K(s) + F_2(g) \longrightarrow 2K^+F^-(s)$

  and, $Mg(s) + Cl_2(g) \longrightarrow Mg^{2+}(Cl^-)_2(s)$

- Hydrogen can combine with reactive metals to form ionic compounds containing the hydride ion, H^-.

  e.g. $2Na(s) + H_2(g) \longrightarrow 2Na^+H^-(s)$

- Although elements widely separated in group position in the Periodic Table are likely to form ionic compounds rather than covalent compounds, this division into pure types of bonding is not justified.

- Combination of atoms of different elements usually results in the formation of compounds with part-ionic character and part-covalent character.

  e.g. aluminium chloride dimer – Al_2Cl_6 – displays both covalent and ionic characteristics.

The mole in earlier studies

- A relative atomic mass scale compares the masses of atoms of the elements.
  e.g. H = 1, He = 4, O = 16, S = 32

Can you see that atoms of helium are four times heavier than atoms of hydrogen and sulphur atoms are twice as heavy as oxygen atoms?

- One mole (1 mol) of a chemical substance was expressed as the amount of substance whose mass in grams is the same as its relative formula mass.
  e.g.
  water, H_2O Relative formula mass $= 1 + 1 + 16$
  $= 18$
  $\Rightarrow$ 1 mole (1 mol) $H_2O = 18$ g

- The mole is linked mainly to the topics within chemistry involving calculations.

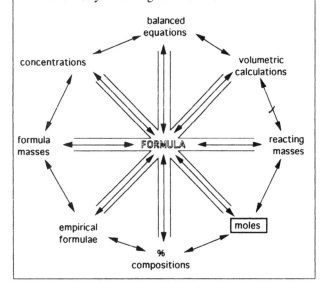

The mole at Higher Grade

"The definition of a mole (1 mol) which is appropriate for your present level of chemistry is, ' that amount of a given substance of a system which contains as many elementary entities as there are carbon atoms in 12 g of carbon-12'.

Quite a statement! What does it mean?"

- The number of specified elementary entities in 1 mol of any substance is the same (6.02×10^{23}) and it is called the Avogadro Constant (symbol L).

- $L = 6.02 \times 10^{23}$ mol^{-1}

- The elementary entities must be specified and may be atoms, molecules, ions or electrons*.

  12 g C contains 6.02×10^{23} atoms mol^{-1}

  16 g CH_4 contains 6.02×10^{23} molecules mol^{-1}

  58.5 g NaCl contains 6.02×10^{23} ion-pairs mol^{-1}

- * The charge on one electron is 1.6×10^{-19}C and so $(6.02 \times 10^{23}) \times (1.6 \times 10^{-19}) = 96500$ C is the charge associated with 1 mol of electrons!

  (96500 C = 1 Faraday = 1 F)

Mole "flow diagram"

It is quite clear that a number of students have real problems applying the Avogadro Constant and related features to mole calculations!

*So, come on! **Get to know the content of this unit very well indeed!***

Look closely at the relationships between "Moles" and the "Avogadro Constant"

Let 'e' equal the number of electrons in an ion	Let 'n' equal the number of ions in the formula unit	Let 'n' equal the number of atoms in a molecule	Let 'p' equal the number of protons in an atom	Let 'e' equal the number of electrons in an atom
$e \times 6.02 \times 10^{23}$ electrons	$n \times 6.02 \times 10^{23}$ ions	$n \times 6.02 \times 10^{23}$ atoms	$p \times 6.02 \times 10^{23}$ protons	$e \times 6.02 \times 10^{23}$ electrons

6.02×10^{23} formula units 6.02×10^{23} molecules 6.02×10^{23} atoms

6.02×10^{23} "entities" ——— 6.02×10^{23} electrons ——— 1 Faraday

96500 C

Relative formula mass (in grams) ◄——— **1 Mol** ———► for gases only ———► One mol has the **same volume** under the **same conditions of temperature and pressure.**

Having problems?

OK - so you now have a much better understanding of the mole and the Avogadro Constant!
Now, you must develop good habits and set out each and every answer to mole calculations in a clear and logical manner!

Even answers to the simplest types of question asking about numbers of atoms, molecules or ions in a certain mass of a chemical substance deserve presentation in a clear style!

Some suggestions for dealing with presentation and layout of answers are provided here and over the next few pages but first, a few words of caution!

Remember to read each question carefully! Do not rush out with a quick guessed response!

Are the questions dealing with numbers of atoms in individual molecules of a substance or in moles of the substance?
e.g.

> **ADVICE   FILE**
>
> " Your notes or textbook will sometimes refer to L atoms or L molecules, etc. This is the use of the symbol L for the Avogadro Constant, $6.02 \times 10^{23} \text{ mol}^{-1}$.
>
> i.e. 6.02×10^{23} atoms = L atoms,
> => 3.01×10^{23} atoms = 0.5 L atoms "

1 molecule of O_2 has 2 oxygen atoms

1 mol O_2 has 6.02×10^{23} (L) oxygen molecules
1 mol O_2 has $2 \times 6.02 \times 10^{23}$ (2 L) oxygen atoms

and,

1 molecule of CH_4 has — 1 C atom / 4 H atoms / Total = 5 atoms

1 mol CH_4 has — 1 mol (L) C atoms / 4 mol (4 L) H atoms / Total = 5 mol (5 L) atoms

Remember, too, that your attempts to display information logically as you work your way through a problem in examination questions may also result in the award of partial marks even when you fail to reach a final answer!

Here is a very simple, but effective, way of showing that you know and understand the terms involved when dealing with a molecular compound such as methane!

Relative Formula Mass/g ——> 1 mol ——> has the Avogadro Constant of molecules ——> n × Avogadro Constant of atoms (n = no. of atoms per molecule)

16 g CH_4 ——> 1 mol CH_4 ——> 6.02×10^{23} molecules ——> $5 \times 6.02 \times 10^{23}$ atoms

= 3.01×10^{24} atoms

When dealing with problems on ionic formulae, remember you are not dealing with either atoms or molecules but "formula units" and ions!
e.g.

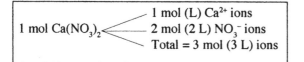

1 mol $Ca(NO_3)_2$ — 1 mol (L) Ca^{2+} ions / 2 mol (2 L) NO_3^- ions / Total = 3 mol (3 L) ions

1 mol $Mg_3(PO_4)_2$ — 3 mol (3 L) Mg^{2+} ions / 2 mol (2 L) PO_4^{3-} ions / Total = 5 mol (5 L) ions

Information on the composition of an ionic substance such as sodium chloride could be set out as follows:

Relative Formula Mass/g ——> 1 mol ——> has the Avogadro Constant of formula units ——> n × Avogadro Constant of ions (n = no. of ions per formula unit)

58.5 g NaCl ——> 1 mol ——> 6.02×10^{23} Na^+Cl^- units ——> $2 \times 6.02 \times 10^{23}$ ions

= 1.204×10^{24} ions

Calculation browser

OK! Clear your desk, settle down and carefully browse this selection of worked examples based on typical questions from exams and assessments!

Remember, too, all the advice given on the importance of good presentation and layout!

I NEVER FORGET!

Example 1   Comparing 1 g water and 1 g propane, C_3H_8, decide which substance has
(i)   more molecules,
(ii)   more atoms.

$18 \text{ g } H_2O \longrightarrow 1 \text{ mol} \qquad \longrightarrow 6.02 \times 10^{23} \text{ molecules} \qquad \longrightarrow \qquad 3 \times 6.02 \times 10^{23} \text{ atoms}$
$1 \text{ g } H_2O \longrightarrow 1/18 \text{ mol} \longrightarrow (1/18) \times 6.02 \times 10^{23} \text{ molecules} \qquad \longrightarrow \qquad (3/18) \times 6.02 \times 10^{23} \text{ atoms}$
$$= (1/6) \times 6.02 \times 10^{23} \text{ atoms}$$

$44 \text{ g } C_3H_8 \qquad \longrightarrow 1 \text{ mol} \qquad \longrightarrow 6.02 \times 10^{23} \text{ molecules} \qquad \longrightarrow \qquad 11 \times 6.02 \times 10^{23} \text{ atoms}$
$1 \text{ g } C_3H_8 \qquad \longrightarrow 1/44 \text{ mol} \longrightarrow (1/44) \times 6.02 \times 10^{23} \text{ molecules} \longrightarrow (11/44) \times 6.02 \times 10^{23} \text{ atoms}$
$$= (1/4) \times 6.02 \times 10^{23} \text{ atoms}$$

1 g water contains more molecules but fewer atoms than 1 g propane.

Example 2   Calculate the mass of 1 atom of carbon.
You may wish to rearrange the presentation order in some cases to be more logical!

$6.02 \times 10^{23} \text{ carbon atoms} \qquad \longrightarrow \qquad 1 \text{ mol} \qquad \longrightarrow \qquad 12 \text{ g}$
$1 \qquad \text{carbon atom} \qquad \underline{\hspace{8cm}} \longrightarrow \qquad \dfrac{12 \times 1}{6.02 \times 10^{23}} \text{ g}$

$$= 1.99 \times 10^{-23} \text{ g}$$

Example 3   Calculate the number of protons in 3.2 g of oxygen gas.
Oxygen gas contains diatomic molecules, $O_2 \longrightarrow$ each atom of oxygen (Atomic Number 8) has 8 protons

$32 \text{ g } O_2 \longrightarrow 1 \text{ mol} \longrightarrow 6.02 \times 10^{23} \text{ molecules} \longrightarrow 2 \times 6.02 \times 10^{23} \text{ atoms} \rightarrow 8 \times 2 \times 6.02 \times 10^{23} \text{ protons}$
$3.2 \text{ g } O_2 \underline{\hspace{10cm}} \rightarrow (3.2/32) \times 8 \times 2 \times 6.02 \times 10^{23} \text{ protons}$
$$= 9.63 \times 10^{23} \text{ protons}$$

Example 4   Calculate the number of ions in 2.64 g of ammonium sulphate.
Ammonium sulphate $(NH_4)_2SO_4 \longrightarrow$ each formula unit contains three ions
$1 \text{ mol } (NH_4)_2SO_4 = 2[14 + (4 \times 1)] + 32 + (4 \times 16) = 132 \text{ g}$

$132 \text{ g } (NH_4)_2SO_4 \longrightarrow 1 \text{ mol} \qquad \longrightarrow 6.02 \times 10^{23} \text{ formula units} \longrightarrow 3 \times 6.02 \times 10^{23} \text{ ions}$
$2.64 \text{ g } (NH_4)_2SO_4 \underline{\hspace{8cm}} \rightarrow (2.64/132) \times 3 \times 6.02 \times 10^{23} \text{ ions}$
$$= 3.6 \times 10^{22} \text{ ions}$$

Example 5   Calculate the mass of potassium phosphate which contains 3.6×10^{22} phosphate ions.

To some students this could appear to be a very difficult calculation! Their main "problem" is, however, that they do not know where to start!
Well, firstly, a correct formula is essential to identify the entities present! Once identified, the mass of these entities may be obtained using relative formula masses for the component elements.

Potassium phosphate has the formula $K_3PO_4 \longrightarrow$ each formula unit contains one phosphate ion
$1 \text{ mol } K_3PO_4 = (3 \times 39) + 31 + (4 \times 16) = 212 \text{ g}$

$1 \text{ mol } K_3PO_4 \longrightarrow 6.02 \times 10^{23} \text{ formula units} \longrightarrow 6.02 \times 10^{23} \text{ phosphate ions} \longrightarrow 212 \text{ g } K_3PO_4$

$3.6 \times 10^{22} \text{ phosphate ions} \longrightarrow \dfrac{212 \times 3.6 \times 10^{22}}{6.02 \times 10^{23}} \text{ g } K_3PO_4$

$$= 12.68 \text{ g}$$

Are things becoming clearer or are you still "having problems"?

Molar volume of a gas

- The molar volume of a gas is the volume occupied by 1 mol of the gas entities at a stated temperature and pressure.

- Molar volume $= \dfrac{\text{mass}}{\text{density}}$

- Molar volume for all gases at room temperature (25 °C) and normal pressure (1 atmosphere) is about 24 dm^3 mol^{-1} (cubic decimetres per mol).

- Molar gas volumes are often stated at *standard temperature and pressure* (O °C and 1 atmosphere) when the value is about 22.4 dm^3 mol^{-1}.

- Avogadro's hypothesis (1811) states that: "Equal volumes of all gases, under the same conditions of temperature and pressure, contain equal numbers of molecules." (For noble gases, 'molecule' = 'atom'.)

- Significantly, the application of Avogadro's hypothesis in calculations dealing with gases means that there can be an interchange of moles and volume.
  e.g.

	$N_2(g)$	+	$3H_2(g)$	$\longrightarrow$	$2NH_3(g)$
	1 mol		3 mol	$\longrightarrow$	2 mol
or	1 vol		3 vol	$\longrightarrow$	2 vol
=>	25 cm^3		75 cm^3	$\longrightarrow$	50 cm^3
=>	10 cm^3		30 cm^3	$\longrightarrow$	20 cm^3
=>	1.5 dm^3		4.5 dm^3	$\longrightarrow$	3.0 dm^3

   (or any quantities which are in proportion)

In problems dealing with reacting masses of gases, you can interchange mass and volume using gas densities which will either be provided within the stem of the question or which may be found in the Data Booklet.

- Density $= \dfrac{\text{mass}}{\text{volume}}$

Data booklet units may be either g cm^{-3} or kg m^{-3}.

Using the density of oxygen given in the Data Booklet, calculate the molar volume of oxygen. (Density of oxygen = 0.0014 g cm^{-3})

Molar mass (1 mol) of O_2 = 2 × 16 = 32 g

Molar volume of $O_2 = \dfrac{\text{Molar mass}}{\text{density}}$

$= \dfrac{32}{0.0014}$ = 22857 cm^3

= 22.86 dm^3

Mole interrelationships

You must keep the interrelationships in mind when tackling all types of calculation!

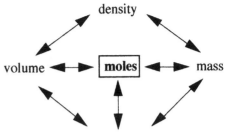

If you know the number of moles of a substance, you can find the mass or the number of entities, and if you also know the density of the substance, you can find the appropriate volume.

More calculations to browse

Calculate the volume of 5 mol oxygen gas if 8 g of the gas molecules occupy 5.8 dm^3 at the same temperature and pressure.

32 g O_2	=	1 mol
=> 8 g O_2	=	0.25 mol

0.25 mol oxygen occupies 5.8 dm^3
=> 5 mol occupies 5.8 × 5/0.25 dm^3
= 116 dm^3

Calculate the number of molecules in 5 cm^3 of hydrogen gas.
(Use the density value in the Data Booklet.)

Density of hydrogen = 0.00009 g cm^{-3}
=> Mass of 5 cm^3 hydrogen = 5 × 0.00009 g
= 0.00045 g

1 mol $H_2 \longrightarrow$ 2 g $\longrightarrow 6.02 \times 10^{23}$ molecules

If, 2 g $H_2 \longrightarrow 6.02 \times 10^{23}$ molecules
=> 0.00045 g $H_2 \longrightarrow \dfrac{6.02 \times 10^{23} \times 0.00045}{2}$
$= 1.355 \times 10^{20}$ molecules

Calculate the density of nitrogen (in g cm^{-3}) taking its molar volume as 22.4 dm^3 mol^{-1}.
Density = mass/volume
Mass of 1 mol N_2 = 28 g
Volume occupied by 28 g N_2 = 22400 cm^3
=> Density = 28/22400 = 0.00125 g cm^{-3}

Calculate the number of atoms in 5 cm^3 lead.

Density of lead = 11.3 g cm^{-3}
=> 5 cm^3 lead has a mass = 5 ×11.3 g = 56.5 g
207 g Pb –>1 mol –> 6.02×10^{23} atoms
=> 56.5 g Pb $\longrightarrow \dfrac{6.02 \times 10^{23} \times 56.5}{207}$ atoms
$= 1.64 \times 10^{23}$ atoms

Calculations based on equations

Many students struggling with chemical calculations just skip over questions of this type immediately "blowing" the chance of a good "A" pass!

You must make a real effort to attempt all these questions and adopt a style and a layout similar to those already suggested!

Your main "problem" is that you need a balanced chemical equation but this is often given!

The balanced chemical equation not only indicates correct formulae, but reacting amounts in moles (and therefore masses) and, if gases, the volumes involved.

What mass of carbon dioxide is produced by completely burning 12 g of methane in air?

$$\text{methane} + \text{oxygen} \longrightarrow \text{carbon dioxide} + \text{water}$$
$$CH_4 \quad + \quad 2O_2 \quad \longrightarrow \quad CO_2 \quad + \quad 2H_2O$$

1 mol	2 mol		1 mol	2 mol

16 g $\longrightarrow$ 44 g

=> 12 g $\longrightarrow$ 44 × 12/16 g

= 33 g

What mass of ammonia may be produced theoretically from 7 kg of nitrogen?

Immediately, the unusual mass for the nitrogen starts a panic!!
But, really, look how easy it is!

$$N_2 \quad + \quad 3H_2 \longrightarrow 2NH_3$$

1 mol   3 mol $\longrightarrow$ 2 mol

28 g $\longrightarrow$ 34 g

=> 28 kg $\longrightarrow$ 34 kg

=> 7 kg $\longrightarrow$ 34 × 7/28 kg

= 8.5 kg

Calculate the mass of potassium chlorate which would produce 3.01×10^{23} molecules of oxygen given:

$$2KClO_3 \longrightarrow 2KCl + 3O_2$$

Mass of 1 mol $KClO_3$ = 39 + 35.5 + (3 × 16)
= 122.5 g

$$2KClO_3 \longrightarrow 2KCl + 3O_2$$

2 mol   2 mol   3 mol

2 × 122.5 g $\longrightarrow$ 3 × 6.02 × 10^{23} oxygen molecules

i.e. 18.06 × 10^{23} O_2 molecules from 245 g $KClO_3$

=> 3.01 × 10^{23} O_2 molecules from

$$\frac{245 \times 3.01 \times 10^{23}}{18.06 \times 10^{23}} \text{ g}$$

= 40.83 g

Reactants in excess

When one of the reactants in a chemical reaction is used up, the reaction ceases.

Any other reactant(s) remaining will be "in excess".

The yield of product depends on the reactant which is not in excess.

Which reactant is in excess when 1.2 g Mg is added to 50 cm³ 1 mol dm⁻³ HCl(aq)?

Remember you must
(i) write a balanced chemical equation,

$$Mg(s) + 2HCl(aq) \longrightarrow MgCl_2(aq) + H_2(g)$$
1 mol   2 mol

i.e. Mg : HCl reacting mol ratio is 1 : 2

(ii) calculate the moles of reactants given.

1 mol Mg = 24 g   => 0.05 mol Mg = 1.2 g
Mols HCl = conc.(mol dm⁻³) × volume (dm³)
= 1 × 0.05 = 0.05 mol

From the balanced equation, 0.05 mol HCl(aq) would react exactly with 0.025 mol Mg (0.6 g). Therefore, with 1.2 g Mg present at the start, it is Mg which is in excess!

Which reactant is in excess when 6.5 g Zn is added to 100 cm³ 2 mol dm⁻³ H₂SO₄(aq)?

$$Zn(s) + H_2SO_4(aq) \longrightarrow ZnSO_4(aq) + H_2(g)$$
1 mol   1 mol

i.e. Zn : H_2SO_4 reacting mol ratio is 1 : 1

1 mol Zn = 65 g   => 0.1 mol Zn = 6.5 g
Mols H_2SO_4 = conc.(mol dm⁻³) × volume (dm³)
= 2 × 0.1 = 0.2 mol

Therefore, H_2SO_4(aq) is in excess by 0.1 mol.

What is the maximum mass of hydrogen that can be obtained when 4.8 g magnesium is added to 200 cm³ 0.5 mol dm⁻³ HCl(aq)?

$$Mg(s) + 2HCl(aq) \longrightarrow MgCl_2(aq) + H_2(g)$$
1 mol   2 mol   1 mol

i.e. Mg : HCl reacting mol ratio is 1 : 2

1 mol Mg = 24 g   => 0.2 mol Mg = 4.8 g
Mols HCl = conc.(mol dm⁻³) × volume (dm³)
= 0.5 × 0.2 = 0.1 mol

The mass of hydrogen given off is determined by the reactant not in excess i.e. the HCl(aq).
From the balanced equation:

2 mol HCl(aq) $\longrightarrow$ 1 mol H_2(g) = 2 g

=> 0.1 mol HCl(aq) $\longrightarrow$ 0.05 mol H_2(g)
= 2 × 0.05 = 0.1 g H_2

Calculations involving volumes

- Avogadro's hypothesis relates moles of gases to volumes.

- There is no common molar volume for solids and no common molar volume for liquids!

- Clearly indicate in calculations involving liquid and solid reactants or products that they have negligible volume. (The use of " – " is common).
  e.g.

$$C(s) \ + \ O_2(g) \longrightarrow CO_2(g)$$
$$\Rightarrow \quad 1 \text{ mol} \quad 1 \text{ mol} \longrightarrow 1 \text{ mol}$$
$$\Rightarrow \quad - \quad 1 \text{ vol} \longrightarrow 1 \text{ vol}$$
$$\Rightarrow \quad - \quad 100 \text{ cm}^3 \longrightarrow 100 \text{ cm}^3$$
(or any volumes in proportion)

and,

$$CH_4(g) + 2O_2(g) \longrightarrow CO_2(g) + 2H_2O(l)$$
$$1 \text{ mol} \quad 2 \text{ mol} \longrightarrow 1 \text{ mol} \quad 2 \text{ mol}$$
$$1 \text{ vol} \quad 2 \text{ vol} \longrightarrow 1 \text{ vol} \quad -$$
$$25 \text{ cm}^3 \quad 50 \text{ cm}^3 \longrightarrow 25 \text{ cm}^3 \quad -$$
(or any volumes in proportion)

Calculate the volume of oxygen required for the complete combustion of 1 g ethene. (The molar volume of oxygen = 24.8 dm³)

$$C_2H_4(g) + 3O_2(g) \longrightarrow 2CO_2(g) + 2H_2O(l)$$
$$1 \text{ mol} \quad 3 \text{ mol}$$
$$28 \text{ g} \quad 3 \times 24.8 \text{ dm}^3$$

$$\Rightarrow \ 28 \text{ g } C_2H_4 \text{ requires } 74.4 \text{ dm}^3 O_2$$
$$\Rightarrow \ 1 \text{ g } C_2H_4 \text{ requires } 74.4 \times 1/28 \text{ dm}^3 O_2$$
$$= 2.66 \text{ dm}^3 O_2$$

Calculate:
  (i) the volume of oxygen required, and
  (ii) the volume of carbon dioxide produced,
when each of the following volumes of gases is burned completely:
  (a) 200 cm³ of methane,
  (b) 2 dm³ of carbon monoxide.

(a) $CH_4(g) + 2O_2(g) \longrightarrow CO_2(g) + 2H_2O(l)$
$\quad$ 1 mol $\quad$ 2 mol $\longrightarrow$ 1 mol $\quad$ 2 mol
$\Rightarrow$ 1 vol $\quad$ 2 vol $\longrightarrow$ 1 vol $\quad$ –
$\Rightarrow$ 200 cm³ **400 cm³** $\longrightarrow$ **200 cm³** –

(b) $2CO(g) + O_2(g) \longrightarrow 2CO_2(g)$
$\quad$ 2 mol $\quad$ 1 mol $\longrightarrow$ 2 mol
$\Rightarrow$ 2 vol $\quad$ 1 vol $\longrightarrow$ 2 vol
$\Rightarrow$ 2 dm³ $\quad$ **1 dm³** $\longrightarrow$ **2 dm³**

If 100 cm³ of butene is burned completely in 800 cm³ of oxygen, what is the composition and volume of the resulting gas mixture?

$$C_4H_8(g) + 6O_2(g) \longrightarrow 4CO_2(g) + 4H_2O(l)$$
$\quad$ 1 mol $\quad$ 6 mol $\longrightarrow$ 4 mol $\quad$ 4 mol
$\Rightarrow$ 1 vol $\quad$ 6 vol $\longrightarrow$ 4 vol $\quad$ –
$\Rightarrow$ 100 cm³ $\quad$ 600 cm³ $\longrightarrow$ 400 cm³ $\quad$ –

From the equation, only 600 cm³ oxygen is required to burn 100 cm³ C_2H_4 i.e. there is an excess of 200 cm³ oxygen.

$\Rightarrow$ The composition of the gas mixture at the end of combustion = 400 cm³ carbon dioxide and 200 cm³ excess oxygen.
$\Rightarrow$ The resulting volume of the gas mixture at the end of combustion = 600 cm³.

Percentage yields

$$\text{Percentage yield} = \frac{\text{actual yield}}{\text{theoretical yield}} \times 100 \ \%$$

In the Haber process, 15 kg of hydrogen reacts with excess nitrogen to produce 3 kg of ammonia.
Calculate the percentage yield.

$$N_2(g) + 3H_2(g) \longrightarrow 2NH_3(g)$$
$\quad$ 1 mol $\quad$ 3 mol $\longrightarrow$ 2 mol
$\Rightarrow \quad 3 \times (1+1)\text{g} \longrightarrow 2 \times (14+3)\text{g}$
$\Rightarrow \quad 6 \text{ g} \longrightarrow 34 \text{ g}$
$\Rightarrow \quad 6 \text{ kg} \longrightarrow 34 \text{ kg}$
$\Rightarrow \quad 15 \text{ kg} \longrightarrow 34 \times 15/6 \text{ kg}$
$\quad\quad\quad\quad\quad = 85 \text{ kg}$
% Yield = actual /theoretical × 100%
$\quad\quad = (3/85) \times 100 \ \%$
$\quad\quad = 3.53 \ \%$

The percentage yield of an ester is only 20% in the following reaction:

$$CH_3COOH + CH_3OH \longrightarrow CH_3COOCH_3 + H_2O$$

What mass of ester will be obtained by reacting 1 mol of CH_3COOH with 1 mol of CH_3OH?

Theoretically,

$$CH_3COOH + CH_3OH \longrightarrow CH_3COOCH_3 + H_2O$$
$\quad$ 1 mol $\quad$ 1 mol $\quad$ 1 mol $\quad$ 1 mol
$\Rightarrow$ 60 g $\quad$ 32 g $\longrightarrow$ 74 g $\quad$ 18 g

i.e. For a 100% yield, 1 mol "reactants" $\longrightarrow$ 74 g ester

$\Rightarrow$ For a 20% yield, mass of ester $= \dfrac{20 \times 74}{100}$ g

$$= 14.8 \text{ g}$$

UNIT 2 The World of Carbon

Fuels

- A fuel is a chemical which is burned to provide energy e.g. coal, oil, natural gas, petrol, etc.

- Natural gas and coal can be used directly as fuels.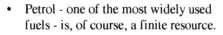

- Crude oil and natural gas products are tailored to specific requirements before being used as fuels.

Petrol

- Petrol - one of the most widely used fuels - is, of course, a finite resource.

- Crude oil distillation provides the fractions which, after modification, produce modern day petrol.

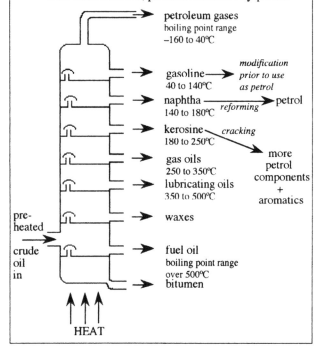

petroleum gases
boiling point range
−160 to 40°C

gasoline → *modification prior to use as petrol*
40 to 140°C

naphtha ——*reforming*——→ petrol
140 to 180°C

kerosine ——*cracking*
180 to 250°C
→ more petrol components + aromatics

gas oils
250 to 350°C

lubricating oils
350 to 500°C

waxes

pre-heated

crude oil in

fuel oil
boiling point range over 500°C

bitumen

HEAT

Reforming

- Reforming involves a set of processes each of which alters the arrangement of atoms in the molecules without necessarily changing the size of the molecules.

- Most aromatic hydrocarbons now come from the reforming of the naphtha fraction.

- Reforming processes can convert the naphtha fraction (containing alkanes and cycloalkanes) to benzene and methylbenzene (toluene).
  e.g.

$$C_6H_{14} \longrightarrow C_6H_6 + 4H_2$$
hexane   benzene

$$C_7H_{14} \longrightarrow C_6H_5CH_3 + 3H_2$$
cycloheptane   methylbenzene
(toluene)

Reforming for better fuels

- Petrol/air mixtures within engines are ignited by sparks from spark plugs.

- C_6 and higher hydrocarbons can be reformed to branched-chain molecules and aromatics which burn more smoothly in petrol engines than their straight-chain isomers.

e.g. $CH_3CH_2CH_2CH_2CH_2CH_2CH_2CH_3$
octane (straight-chain alkane)

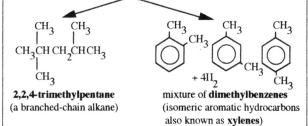

2,2,4-trimethylpentane
(a branched-chain alkane)

mixture of **dimethylbenzenes**
(isomeric aromatic hydrocarbons also known as **xylenes**)

- Octane ratings (numbers) are relative values of the ability of a fuel to burn smoothly and not cause "knocking" (auto-ignition of petrol/air mixtures when compressed) within engines.

Hydrocarbon	Octane Rating/Number
heptane	0
cyclohexane	83
2,2,4-trimethylpentane	100
1,2-dimethylbenzene	107

- The most effective "anti-knock" agent for use in petrol has been tetraethyl-lead, $Pb(C_2H_5)_4$.

- Since leaded petrol gives rise to several polluting exhaust products (lead, unburnt hydrocarbons, CO and NO_x), as part of a European strategy to reduce pollution from road traffic, leaded petrol has been banned from general sale since 1/1/2000! Lead replacement petrol (LRP) and Anti-Wear Additive (AWA) contain alternatives to lead to protect engine parts from excessive wear.

- Unleaded petrol with a resistance to auto-ignition requires components which have a greater degree of molecular branching and/or aromatic content.

Petrol change, sir?

- Unseen, and probably undetected by the motorist, are the summer/winter petrol supply changes.

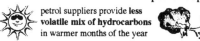 petrol suppliers provide **less volatile mix of hydrocarbons** in warmer months of the year

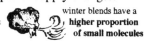 winter blends have a **higher proportion of small molecules**

- Oxygenates - fuels with oxygen in their molecules - can increase the octane number of petrol.

e.g.

H
|
H—C—O—H
|
H methanol

H H
| |
H—C—C—O—H
| |
H H ethanol

H CH₃
| |
H—C—C—O—CH₃
| |
H CH₃ MTBE (an ether)

- Replacement of aromatic and butane components of petrol by oxygenates can lead to high octane/ "low knock" petrols which create less pollution.

Other fuels

- Since present supplies of crude oil and natural gas are still relatively cheap, conversion to alternative fuels is essential for transport in the future.

- Liquefied petroleum gas (LPG) - a mixture mainly of propane, C_3H_8, and butane, C_4H_{10}, can be used in cars if engine modifications can be made.

  DANGER
  Highly
  flammable LPG

- Sugar cane is a "renewable" source of ethanol, C_2H_5OH, for blending with engine fuel in countries where it can be produced economically.

- Ethanol burns cleanly in car engines.
  $$C_2H_5OH + 3O_2 \longrightarrow 2CO_2 + 3H_2O$$

- Chemists are taking a serious look at methanol as a likely fuel to replace petrol although there are both advantages and disadvantages recognised at the present time.

- Methanol (octane number 114) is not as volatile as petrol but burns very cleanly in car engines.
  $$CH_3OH + 1\tfrac{1}{2}O_2 \longrightarrow CO_2 + 2H_2O$$

- Methanol is made presently in a fairly economical industrial process from a mixture of CO and H_2 in a ratio of 1 : 2.
  $$CO + 2H_2 \longrightarrow CH_3OH$$

- Methanol (used as an oxygenate) is not very miscible when blended with petrol although additives can help to reduce this problem.

- More serious is the ability of methanol/petrol mixtures to absorb water vapour which could extensively corrode expensive engine parts.

- Some biological materials e.g. farm animal waste and sewage, under anaerobic ("without air") conditions, are fermented to produce "Biogas".

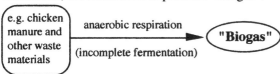

e.g. chicken manure and other waste materials → anaerobic respiration (incomplete fermentation) → "Biogas"

- "Biogas" – a gaseous fuel mixture comprising mainly methane, CH_4, – may soon increase in commercial importance as North Sea gas supplies dwindle.

- The continued use of diesel fuel is another problem requiring speedy and effective solution.

- In diesel engines, compression of the hot diesel/air mixtures bring about spontaneous ignition.

- More efficient, with exhaust emissions of CO at around one-tenth that of petrol engines, diesel engines produce more smoke, odour and risk to health due to higher proportions of aromatic hydrocarbons present. Benzene is *carcinogenic*.

Hydrogen - fuelling the future?

- The attractiveness of hydrogen as a fuel is based on the high energy released per unit mass burned and the non-polluting nature of the combustion product (no CO_2 released to the atmosphere!)
  $$H_2 + \tfrac{1}{2}O_2 \longrightarrow H_2O$$

- Future technologies may develop an economic process for separating hydrogen from sea water by electrolysis using solar, wave, nuclear, or some other forms of energy.
  $$2H_2O(l) + 2e^- \longrightarrow H_2(g) + 2OH^-(aq)$$

- Hydrogen piped ashore would be used as heating fuel, a raw material for chemical industries or in fuel cells (with oxygen) producing electricity.

- While chemical industries can store and handle hydrogen safely, using it as a fuel in small, moving vehicles is another matter!

- Hydrogen is already being used in experimental vehicles but a number of difficulties have to be overcome before its ease of use matches that of petrol e.g. fuel tanks are large and heavy for the relatively small quantity of hydrogen gas on board!

- Although hydrogen may be liquefied for vehicles to carry more fuel, the high pressures (over 100 atmospheres) and extreme cold of the liquid fuel (–253 °C) in very large and heavy vessels will present a number of safety and design problems!

- Much energy will also be consumed in liquefying the hydrogen gas under pressure. Will this defeat the purpose of trying to produce a more "energy efficient" fuel?

- If, however, hydrogen can be made where it is to be consumed, the storage problem disappears!

- Hydrogen can be made to combine directly with some metals to produce solid ionic hydrides. e.g.
  $$Ca(s) + H_2(g) \longrightarrow Ca^{2+}(H^-)_2(s)$$

  Can you see how hydrogen atoms can become H^- ions by gaining electrons? Can you also see that the H^- ion is isoelectronic with a helium atom?

- Calcium hydride can release hydrogen gas either by thermal decomposition or reaction with water.
  $$CaH_2(s) \longrightarrow Ca(s) + H_2(g)$$
  or,
  $$CaH_2(s) + 2H_2O(l) \longrightarrow 2H_2(g) + Ca(OH)_2(aq)$$

- Perhaps the internal combustion engine of the future, using hydrogen as a fuel, will be developed from more easily handled, solid metal hydrides?

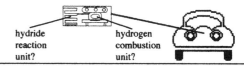

hydride reaction unit?   hydrogen combustion unit?

Nomenclature and structural formulae

The IUPAC convention for the systematic naming of organic compounds covers all homologous series.

In the notes which follow, you will see examples of the convention applied to molecules of alkanes, alkenes, alkynes, alkanols, alkanals, alkanones, alkanoic acids and esters. You will also be able to distinguish clearly between molecular formulae and structural formulae - full and shortened.

Saturated hydrocarbons

Alkanes

*   The first three alkanes are methane, ethane and propane with **molecular formulae** CH_4, C_2H_6 and C_3H_8, respectively.

*   **Structural formulae** of these alkanes are shown by:

    methane   ethane   propane

*   **Shortened structural formulae** are used to show how atoms are grouped within molecules without drawing the covalent bond 'lines'

    e.g. CH_3CH_3 $CH_3CH_2CH_3$
          ethane   propane

*   Higher homologues exhibit isomerism and show the systematic naming convention at work. Butane, C_4H_{10}, has two isomeric forms:

    butane   2-methylpropane

    $CH_3CH_2CH_2CH_3$ $CH_3CH(CH_3)CH_3$

*   Pentane, C_5H_{12}, has three isomers:

    pentane   2-methylbutane   2,2-dimethylpropane

    $CH_3CH_2CH_2CH_2CH_3$ $CH_3CH(CH_3)CH_2CH_3$ $CH_3C(CH_3)_2CH_3$

You should practise systematic names and structural formulae - full and shortened - for the first eight alkanes. Remember your prefixes help!

Meth = 1 'carbon atom'
Eth = 2 'carbon atoms'
Prop = 3 'carbon atoms'
But = 4 'carbon atoms'
Pent = 5 'carbon atoms'
Hex = 6 'carbon atoms'
Hept = 7 'carbon atoms'
Oct = 8 'carbon atoms'

The molecule shown above has molecular formula C_6H_{14} and is 2-methylpentane **not** 4-methylpentane.

The shortened structural formula of this isomer of hexane is represented as:

$$CH_3CH(CH_3)CH_2CH_2CH_3$$

Cycloalkanes

*   Cyclopropane, C_3H_6, and cyclobutane, C_4H_8, are small, rather unstable "ring" compounds.

*   The easiest cycloalkanes to obtain are the more stable 5- and 6-membered "ring" compounds.

    cyclopentane   cyclohexane

*   The cycloalkanes are isomeric with the alkenes.

Unsaturated hydrocarbons

*   Functional groups are groups of atoms within molecules with characteristic chemical reactivity.

*   Alkene molecules have $>C=C<$ bonds present.

*   Alkyne molecules have $-C\equiv C-$ bonds present.

Alkenes

*   The first two alkenes are ethene and propene with molecular formulae C_2H_4 and C_3H_6, respectively.

*   Full and shortened structural formulae of these alkenes are shown by:

    ethene   propene

    $CH_2 = CH_2$ $CH_2 = CHCH_3$

*   Higher alkene homologues exhibit isomerism and the systematic naming convention indicates the position of the functional group in a molecule.

    but-1-ene   but-2-ene   methylpropene

    $CH_2 = CHCH_2CH_3$ $CH_3CH = CHCH_3$ $CH_2 = C(CH_3)CH_3$

Alkynes

*   The most important members of this series are ethyne, propyne, but-1-yne and but-2-yne.

ethyne	propyne
$H-C\equiv C-H$	$H-C\equiv C-\overset{H}{\underset{H}{C}}-H$
$HC\equiv CH$	$HC\equiv CCH_3$
but-1-yne	but-2-yne
$H-C\equiv C-\overset{H}{\underset{H}{C}}-\overset{H}{\underset{H}{C}}-H$	$H-\overset{H}{\underset{H}{C}}-C\equiv C-\overset{H}{\underset{H}{C}}-H$
$HC\equiv CCH_2CH_3$	$CH_3C\equiv CCH_3$

You are expected to be able to handle names and structures of alkenes/alkynes to C_8 molecular size.

*   Industrial chemists and college lecturers still use trivial names e.g. ethene is known as *ethylene*, and ethyne is known as *acetylene*.

Alkanes – sources and uses

- Alkanes (obtained from fractional distillation of oil) display a regular increase in boiling point with increasing molecular size. They are used as fuels.

- Alkane molecules C_1 to C_4 are gases, C_5 to C_{17} are normally liquids, and $> C_{17}$ are normally solids.

- Natural gas contains mainly methane, CH_4, and ethane, C_2H_6, in varying proportions which can be separated for specific uses.

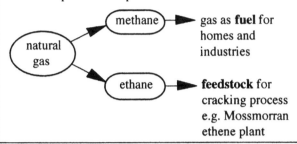

Cycloalkanes – sources and uses

- The smaller members of this series are made in the laboratory but cyclohexane, C_6H_{12}, and cycloheptane, C_7H_{14}, are found in mineral oils.

- Cyclohexane is used as an industrial solvent.

The cycloalkanes tend to resemble the normal alkanes in their chemical reactions.

Alkenes – sources and uses

- Ethene and propene are made by cracking naphtha.

- Ethene is also produced in Fife, at Mossmorran, by cracking ethane obtained from natural gas.

$$CH_3 - CH_3 \longrightarrow CH_2 = CH_2 + H_2$$

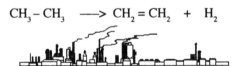

- Propene can be produced by cracking propane (also found in natural gas).

$$CH_3 - CH_2 - CH_3 \longrightarrow CH_2 = CH - CH_3 + H_2$$

- The cracking of alkenes described above involves the dehydrogenation of alkane molecules.

- Alkenes are feedstocks of major importance in the production of addition polymers (plastics).

e.g. polypropene production

$$\begin{array}{cccc} CH_3 & H & CH_3 & H & CH_3 & H \\ & C = C & & C = C & & C = C \\ H & & H & H & & H & H & & H \end{array} \longrightarrow \begin{array}{c} CH_3\ H\ CH_3\ H\ CH_3\ H \\ -C-C-C-C-C-C- \\ H\ \ H\ \ H\ \ H\ \ H\ \ H \end{array}$$

propene monomers   part of a polypropene chain

When CH_3 groups are all lying on the "same side" of the main C – C chain, this structure results in a tough, crystalline product called *isotactic* polypropene, used in fibre and transparent film production. Polypropenes with CH_3 groups arranged alternatively (*syndiotactic*), or arranged quite randomly (*atactic*), on the main C – C chain are possible by altering the polymerisation process conditions.

- But-1-ene polymerises to *isotactic* polybut-1-ene, a high tensile strength polymer with high breakage resistance used in the manufacture of tubing.

Alkynes – sources and uses

- The role of ethyne (an unstable gas) in industrial chemistry was once very great but it has been diminished by the present availability of ethene.

- A mixture of ethyne (*acetylene*) and oxygen generates a temperature close to 3000 °C when burned making this useful for the cutting and welding of steel.

Alkanes – reactions

- Alkanes used mainly as fuels burn completely in oxygen to form CO_2 and H_2O as the only products.

e.g. octane (in petrols)

$$C_8H_{18} + 12\tfrac{1}{2}O_2 \longrightarrow 8CO_2 + 9H_2O$$

- Alkanes tend to undergo substitution reactions in the presence of light or catalysts.

$$\text{e.g.} \quad CH_4 + Cl_2 \longrightarrow CH_3Cl + HCl$$
methane   chlorine   chloromethane   hydrogen chloride

- Cracking in the laboratory produces a mixture of saturated and unsaturated hydrocarbons.

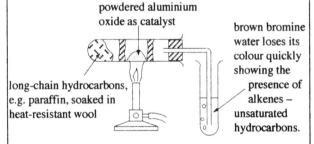

powdered aluminium oxide as catalyst

long-chain hydrocarbons, e.g. paraffin, soaked in heat-resistant wool

brown bromine water loses its colour quickly showing the presence of alkenes – unsaturated hydrocarbons.

- The mixture of products from cracking is due to the breaking of different bonds in the alkanes.

$$\text{e.g.} \quad C_{10}H_{22} \longrightarrow C_3H_8 + C_7H_{14}$$
decane   propane   heptene

$$\longrightarrow C_8H_{18} + C_2H_4$$
octane   ethene

Alkenes – reactions

- Alkenes are reactive hydrocarbons and undergo addition reactions with diatomic molecules

e.g. with bromine-

$$\begin{array}{c} H\ \ H \\ | \ \ \ | \\ H-C=C-H \end{array} + Br_2 \longrightarrow \begin{array}{c} H\ \ H \\ | \ \ \ | \\ H-C-C-H \\ | \ \ \ | \\ Br\ \ Br \end{array}$$

ethene (unsaturated)   bromine   1,2-dibromoethane (saturated)

and, with hydrogen-

$$\begin{array}{c} H\ \ H \\ | \ \ \ | \\ H-C=C-H \end{array} + H_2 \longrightarrow \begin{array}{c} H\ \ H \\ | \ \ \ | \\ H-C-C-H \\ | \ \ \ | \\ H\ \ H \end{array}$$

ethene (unsaturated)   hydrogen   ethane (saturated)

and, with hydrogen iodide-

$$\begin{array}{c} H\ \ H \\ | \ \ \ | \\ H-C=C-CH_3 \end{array} + HI \longrightarrow \begin{array}{c} H\ \ H \\ | \ \ \ | \\ H-C-C-CH_3 \\ | \ \ \ | \\ H\ \ I \end{array}$$

propene   hydrogen iodide   2-iodopropane

Note: the I atom from HI bonds to the C atom with fewest H atoms. This is called the Markovnikov Rule.

Alkynes - addition reactions

- Alkynes, like alkenes, are unsaturated and can react with several reagents in addition reactions. e.g. with hydrogen-

$$HC \equiv CH \xrightarrow[\text{catalyst}]{H_2 \; Ni} H_2C = CH_2$$

ethyne   ethene

The product of this "first stage" addition, ethene, is unsaturated and can be converted to ethane by a "second stage" addition-

$$H_2C = CH_2 \xrightarrow[\text{catalyst}]{H_2 \; Ni} H_3C - CH_3$$

ethene   ethane

and, with chlorine-

$$HC \equiv CH \xrightarrow{Cl_2} HClC = CClH \xrightarrow{Cl_2} Cl_2HC - CHCl_2$$

ethyne   1,2-dichloroethene   1,1,2,2-tetrachloroethane

and, with hydrogen iodide-

$$HC \equiv CH \xrightarrow{HI} H_2C = CHI \xrightarrow{HI} H_3C - CHI_2$$

ethyne   iodoethene   1,1,-diiodoethane

The "second stage" addition of HI is in accordance with the Markovnikov Rule mentioned earlier.

Aromatic hydrocarbons

- Most aromatic hydrocarbons come from the reforming of naphtha.

- The parent molecule of all aromatic compounds (originally *aroma = fragrant*) is benzene, C_6H_6.

- Benzene is a saturated hydrocarbon with a planar, hexagonal ring structure.

Each carbon atom in the hexagonal ring has three electrons involved in covalent bonding to other atoms. 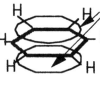 Clouds of delocalised electrons above and below the plane of the "ring" bond the atoms together in a stable structure.

- The structure of benzene is represented by

- The benzene ring resists addition reactions but in the benzene/bromine reaction, one hydrogen atom of benzene is replaced by a bromine atom.

$$C_6H_6 + Br_2 \longrightarrow C_6H_5Br + HBr$$

bromobenzene (phenylbromide)

This is a substitution reaction and the phenyl group, $- C_6H_5$, is represented by the structure opposite.

- At one time, all aromatic hydrocarbons were made from coal!

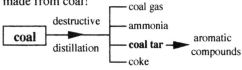

Could there be a return to coal-based chemical industries in an oil-depleted future?

Important aromatics in the chemical industry

- Benzene and its related compounds are very important feedstocks for the chemical industries.

- A feedstock is a chemical from which other chemicals can be extracted or synthesised.

You are not expected to know details of the reagents or the process conditions indicated by arrows in the following diagram which shows some reactions of benzene and its related compounds. However, you would be expected to handle similar information if it was supplied in a "problem solving" situation!

- By substituting (in chemical reactions) one or more hydrogen atoms of a benzene molecule, a wide range of products is available.

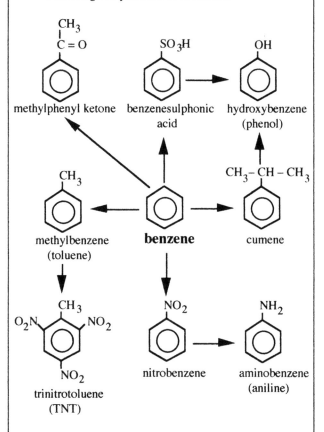

- Many consumer products including medicines, plastics, paints, dyes, detergents, cosmetics and agricultural chemicals are made from these aromatic chemicals.

- Consumer products are generally complex molecules which have been synthesised from smaller, reactive organic compounds. e.g. paracetamol

Substituted alkanes

A number of functional groups can be inserted into alkane molecules by substitution of hydrogen atoms producing several homologous series of compounds.

- You should be able to identify:

  – OH   the hydroxyl group

  – CHO   the aldehyde group

  $>$C = O   the carbonyl group

  – COOH   the carboxyl group

  – COO –   the ester group

  – NH_2 the amine (amino) group

Naming alkanols (alcohols)

- Alcohols are characterised by the –OH group in their molecules and have names ending ' –ol'.

- Alkanols are an homologous series of alcohols (general formula $C_nH_{2n+1}OH$) related to the alkanes and named according to the IUPAC system.

methanol   ethanol   propan-1-ol   propan-2-ol

CH_3OH CH_3CH_2OH $CH_3CH_2CH_2OH$ $CH_3CH(OH)CH_3$

- Alcohols are classified as primary, secondary or tertiary according to the nature of chemical groups adjacent to the hydroxyl group (–OH).

- The general formula for a primary alcohol is RCH_2OH, where R may be a hydrogen atom or an alkyl group i.e. methyl – CH_3, ethyl – C_2H_5, etc.

  Butan-1-ol

  Butan-4-ol is incorrect!

- The general formula for a secondary alcohol is $(R)_2CHOH$, where both R groups are alkyl groups.

  3-methylbutan-2-ol

  2-methylbutan-3-ol is incorrect!

- The general formula for a tertiary alcohol is $(R)_3COH$, where all the R groups are alkyl groups.

  2,3-dimethylbutan-2-ol

  2,3-dimethylbutan-3-ol is incorrect!

- Alkanols may have more than one –OH group.

  Ethane-1,2-diol (also known as ethylene glycol) is found in antifreeze for car radiators.

  Propane-1,2,3-triol (also known as glycerol or glycerine) is found in many medicines e.g. cough remedies with glycerine and honey mixtures.

You should be able to name and draw structures of alkanols and other substituted alkanes to C_8 size.

Ethanol – sources and reactions

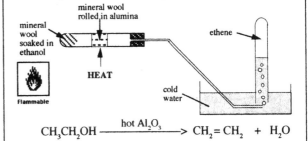

- Ethanol, C_2H_5OH, is the common alcohol in drinks and to meet market demand, ethanol is made by methods other than the fermentation of carbohydrates.

$$C_6H_{12}O_6 \xrightarrow[\text{in yeast}]{\text{enzymes}} 2C_2H_5OH + 2CO_2$$

- Industrial ethanol is manufactured by the catalytic hydration of ethene with steam.

$$CH_2 = CH_2 + H_2O \xrightarrow[\substack{\text{at 300°C under}\\ \text{high pressure}}]{H_3PO_4 \text{ on } SiO_2} CH_3CH_2OH$$

- Dehydration of ethanol produces ethene.

$$CH_3CH_2OH \xrightarrow{\text{hot } Al_2O_3} CH_2=CH_2 + H_2O$$

- Alkanols burn completely in air (oxygen) to produce carbon dioxide and water.

$$C_2H_5OH + 3O_2 \longrightarrow 2CO_2 + 3H_2O$$

Alkanols to alkanals

- Alkanals are a subset of aldehydes named after the corresponding alkanols but ending in '–al'.

  aldehyde functional group

- Only primary alkanols can be **partially oxidised** to alkanals i.e. the alkanol molecule undergoes a loss of two H atoms to form the alkanal molecule.

  methanol CH_3OH oxidation   methanal HCHO

  loss of these H atoms brings about an increase in O:H ratio i.e. oxidation of the compound has taken place

Also,

CH_3CH_2OH ethanol $\longrightarrow$ CH_3CHO ethanal

$CH_3CH_2CH_2OH$ propan-1-ol $\longrightarrow$ CH_3CH_2CHO propanal

$CH_3CH_2CH_2CH_2OH$ butan-1-ol $\longrightarrow$ $CH_3CH_2CH_2CHO$ butanal

- Colour changes occur with suitable lab oxidising agents e.g. acidified permanganate, acidified dichromate and hot copper(II) oxide.

(a) MnO_4^- (purple) $+ 8H^+ + 5e^- \longrightarrow Mn^{2+}$ (colourless) $+ 4H_2O$

(b) $Cr_2O_7^{2-}$ (orange) $+ 14H^+ + 6e^- \longrightarrow 2Cr^{3+}$ (green) $+ 7H_2O$

(c) $Cu^{2+}(s)$ [in CuO(s)] (black) $+ 2e^- \longrightarrow Cu$ (red-brown)

Alkanols to alkanones

- Alkanones are a subset of ketones which take their names from the alkanols but end in '–one'.

- The ketone functional group is the carbonyl group linked to two other carbon groups.

$$-\overset{|}{\underset{|}{C}}-\overset{\overset{O}{\parallel}}{C}-\overset{|}{\underset{|}{C}}-$$

- Only secondary alkanols are oxidised to alkanones.

- Secondary alkanol molecules undergo loss of two hydrogen atoms to form the alkanone.

propan-2-ol
$CH_3CH(OH)CH_3$ — e.g. these H atoms are removed → propanone CH_3COCH_3

Also,

$$CH_3CH_2CH(OH)CH_3 \longrightarrow CH_3CH_2COCH_3$$
butan-2-ol   butanone

- Suitable laboratory oxidising agents for alkanone formation also include acidified permanganate, acidified dichromate and hot copper(II) oxide.

pentan-2-ol $\longrightarrow$ pentan-2-one

and,

pentan-3-ol $\longrightarrow$ pentan-3-one

- Tertiary alkanols are not oxidised to either alkanals or alkanones by this type of treatment.

Aldehyde or ketone?

- While aldehydes tend to have pungent smells and ketones are usually sweeter, tests with laboratory reagents are normally used to distinguish them.

- Aldehydes reduce warm, blue Benedict's solution forming orange-brown copper(I) oxide.

$$Cu^{2+}(aq) + e^- \longrightarrow Cu^+(s) \ [in \ Cu_2O(s)]$$

- Aldehydes reduce warm Tollen's reagent (also known as ammoniacal silver nitrate) forming a "silver mirror".

$$Ag^+(aq) + e^- \longrightarrow Ag(s)$$

- Ketones do **not** reduce Benedict's solution or Tollen's reagent.

Aldehydes to acids by oxidation

- Aldehydes (but not ketones) can be oxidised to compounds called carboxylic acids.

- The aldehyde group, –CHO, undergoes the gain of an oxygen atom to form the carboxyl group, –COOH, the functional group of carboxylic acids.
e.g.

methanal $\xrightarrow[\ [+O]\ ]{oxidation}$ methanoic acid
HCHO → HCOOH

ethanal $\xrightarrow[\ [+O]\ ]{oxidation}$ ethanoic acid
CH_3CHO → CH_3COOH

Can you see why only the aldehyde group – and not the ketone group – can oxidise in this way?

- Ethanoic acid is the best known member of the homologous series known as the alkanoic acids, which also contains:
methanoic acid   HCOOH
propanoic acid CH_3CH_2COOH
butanoic acid $CH_3CH_2CH_2COOH$
pentanoic acid $CH_3CH_2CH_2CH_2COOH$

- Carboxylic acids are weak acids i.e. they are not completely ionised in solution, forming only a few hydrogen ions and carboxylate ions.

$$RCOOH + aq \rightleftharpoons RCOO^-(aq) + H^+(aq)$$

- In industry, some ethanoic acid is produced by bacterial oxidation of ethanol from fermented carbohydrate to make vinegar – a solution of ethanoic acid (~ 5% in water).

- 'Non-brewed condiment' is also a solution of ethanoic acid in water but the acid is not prepared by a fermentation process.

- The bulk of industrially prepared ethanoic acid results from the direct oxidation of the naphtha fraction from crude oil – quite a profitable process, since it produces useful by-products *.

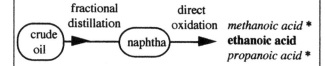

crude oil $\xrightarrow[distillation]{fractional}$ naphtha $\xrightarrow[oxidation]{direct}$ *methanoic acid* * **ethanoic acid** *propanoic acid* *

- Methanoic acid is used in wool dyeing, leather tanning, as a preservative in fruit juices and for disinfecting wooden beer and wine storage casks.

Can you see why methanoic acid would produce a "silver mirror" on testing with warm Tollen's reagent?

- Propanoic acid is employed in the manufacture of some popular drugs for treatment of rheumatism.

Summary of oxidation of alkanols

- Primary alkanol $\xrightarrow{\text{oxidation}}$ alkanal $\xrightarrow{\text{oxidation}}$ alkanoic acid
  RCH_2OH $\qquad$ $RCHO$ $\qquad$ $RCOOH$

- Secondary alkanol $\xrightarrow{\text{oxidation}}$ alkanone
  $(R)_2CHOH$ $\qquad$ $RCOR$

- Tertiary alkanol $\xrightarrow{\text{oxidation}}$ no reaction
  $(R)_3COH$

Remember, reduction is the reverse of oxidation and results in a decrease in the O:H ratio in the carbon compound.

Ester formation (esterification)

- Many alcohols and carboxylic acids used to prepare esters in the laboratory are highly flammable and no naked flame should be present during ester preparation.

Highly Flammable

- Methanol when warmed with methanoic acid (using concentrated H_2SO_4 as a catalyst) forms the ester called methyl methanoate.

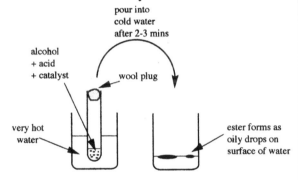

pour into cold water after 2-3 mins

alcohol + acid + catalyst

wool plug

very hot water

ester forms as oily drops on surface of water

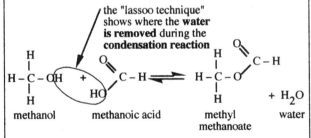

the "lassoo technique" shows where the **water is removed** during the **condensation reaction**

methanol $\qquad$ methanoic acid $\qquad$ methyl methanoate $\qquad$ + H_2O water

- The ester linkage contains oxygen atoms from both the alcohol and the acid molecules.

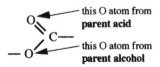

this O atom from **parent acid**

this O atom from **parent alcohol**

- Esters are named appropriately from the parent alcohol and carboxylic acid.

Alcohol	Acid	Ester name	Ester formula
ethanol	ethanoic	ethyl ethanoate	$C_2H_5OOCCH_3$
methanol	propanoic	methyl propanoate	$CH_3OOCC_2H_5$

ADVICE FILE

" Always draw a full structural formula before trying to identify an ester or to name an ester from a shortened structural formula!"

Reversing the process (hydrolysis)

- Esterification is a reversible process.

- Ester hydrolysis, which may be carried out on a laboratory scale, converts an ester into an alcohol and a carboxylic acid.

Apparatus for the laboratory hydrolysis of an ester. e.g. methyl methanoate

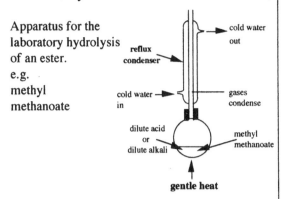

cold water out

reflux condenser

cold water in

gases condense

dilute acid or dilute alkali

methyl methanoate

gentle heat

- The equations for ester hydrolysis also include the reversible reaction sign.

$$CH_3OOCH + H_2O \rightleftharpoons CH_3OH + HCOOH$$
methyl methanoate $\quad$ water $\qquad$ methanol $\quad$ methanoic acid

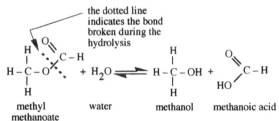

the dotted line indicates the bond broken during the hydrolysis

methyl methanoate $\qquad$ water $\qquad$ methanol $\quad$ methanoic acid

OK – got your ester chemistry clearly worked out?

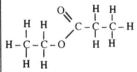

This is ethyl propanoate **not** propyl ethanoate.

Hydrolysis of this ester will give the alkanol, ethanol, and the alkanoic acid, propanoic acid as products.

This is methyl butanoate **not** butyl methanoate.

Hydrolysis of this ester will give the alkanol, methanol, and the alkanoic acid, butanoic acid as products.

Uses of esters

- Many natural flavours and smells are due to volatile ester molecules in fruits and flowers.

- Natural and synthetic esters are used as flavourings in foodstuffs, in medicinal preparations, as solvents for paints and varnishes, and as perfume scents, etc.

Natural products - fats and oils

- Supplies of fats and oils occur in many different plants and animals (including fish and other marine creatures).

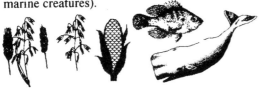

- Animals produce fats – mainly saturated solids or semi-solids – while plants and fish produce mainly unsaturated, liquid oils.

- The large saturated molecules in fats are able to bond tightly within a closely packed structure giving rise to solids.

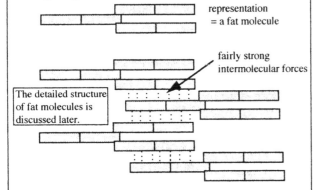

representation = a fat molecule

fairly strong intermolecular forces

The detailed structure of fat molecules is discussed later.

- The unsaturated oil molecules (containing C = C bonds) are shaped in such a way as to prevent close packing of the molecules.

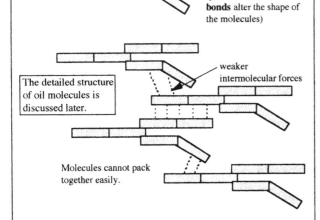

representation = an oil molecule (presence of **C = C bonds** alter the shape of the molecules)

weaker intermolecular forces

The detailed structure of oil molecules is discussed later.

Molecules cannot pack together easily.

- The lower melting points of oils compared to those of fats of similar molecular mass is related to the higher degree of unsaturation present in the oils and to the decrease in strength of the intermolecular forces in oils.

- Naturally occurring fats and oils contain large molecules identified as esters - the condensation products of reactions between alcohols and carboxylic acids.

They are, however, slightly more complex molecules than the simple esters you met earlier!

Esters in oils and fats

- Ester molecules in oils and fats are made from glycerol and fatty acids in the ratio glycerol : fatty acid of 1 : 3.

- Hydrolysis of esters in oils and fats produces glycerol and these fatty acids.

- Glycerol, or propane-1,2,3-triol, is a trihydric alcohol i.e. each molecule has three –OH groups.

The structural formula is usually shown as:

$$H-\underset{H}{\overset{OH}{\underset{|}{\overset{|}{C}}}}-\underset{H}{\overset{OH}{\underset{|}{\overset{|}{C}}}}-\underset{H}{\overset{OH}{\underset{|}{\overset{|}{C}}}}-H \quad \text{or} \quad \begin{array}{l} CH_2-OH \\ | \\ CH-OH \\ | \\ CH_2-OH \end{array}$$

The shortened structural formula is $CH_2(OH)CH(OH)CH_2(OH)$

- Fatty acids are saturated or unsaturated straight-chain carboxylic acids having even numbers of carbon atoms ranging from C_4 to C_{24}, but mainly C_{16} and C_{18}.

e.g.

palmitic acid	$C_{15}H_{31}COOH$	(saturated)
oleic acid	$C_{17}H_{33}COOH$	(unsaturated)
stearic acid	$C_{17}H_{35}COOH$	(saturated)

- Esters formed from glycerol are known as triesters or triglycerides e.g. glyceryl trioleate is typical of the unsaturated esters found in many oils.

Each of the three $C_{17}H_{33}$ chains in the triglyceride molecule has a C = C bond present.

Hydrolysis of each glyceryl trioleate molecule produces one molecule of glycerol and three molecules of oleic acid.

- Glyceryl tristearate is typical of the saturated esters in plant and animal fats.

Each of the three $C_{17}H_{35}$ chains in the triglyceride molecule is saturated.

Hydrolysis of each glyceryl tristearate molecule produces one molecule of glycerol and three molecules of stearic acid.

- Oils and fats are rarely single esters but tend to be mixtures of triglycerides in which the three fatty acid molecules combined with each glycerol molecule may, or may not, be identical.

R, R' and R" represent different chains of bonded carbon and hydrogen atoms which may be either saturated or unsaturated.

- The hydrolysis products from each of the above triglyceride molecules would be one molecule each of glycerol and of the fatty acids RCOOH, R'COOH and R"COOH.

Dietary and health concerns

- Fats and oils in the human diet provide a high energy source (more than double for the same mass of carbohydrate).

- Fats and oils are, however, also known to be essential for metabolic processes of the body.

- Some humans have diets with a high content of fats and oils with, apparently, few health problems!

- In recent years, medical research has suggested that there may be a link between heart disease (high in Scotland) and eating excessive saturated fatty foods.

- It has been suggested that the risk of heart disease is greatly reduced by eating fatty foods containing polyunsaturates i.e. fats with several $C = C$ bonds in their molecules but some recent studies cast some doubt on the strength of this link.

- Generally, vegetable oils are a good source of polyunsaturates and fats are a poor source, although exceptions do exist e.g. coconut oil.

- Unsaturated oils can be saturated by the addition of hydrogen in the presence of a nickel catalyst.

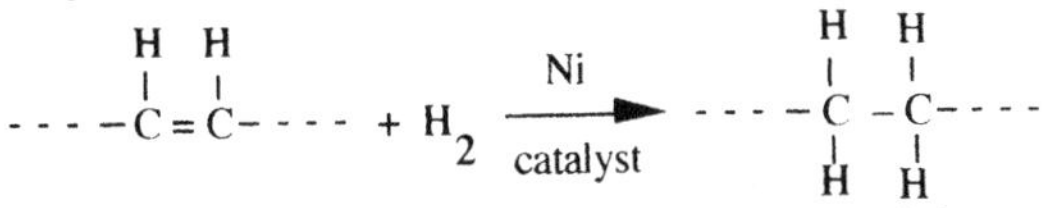

$$- - - \overset{\underset{|}{H}}{C} = \overset{\underset{|}{H}}{C} - - - \ + \ H_2 \quad \xrightarrow[\text{catalyst}]{Ni} \quad - - - - \overset{\underset{|}{H}}{\underset{|}{C}} - \overset{\underset{|}{H}}{\underset{|}{C}} - - -$$

unsaturated site in an "oil molecule"   saturated site in a "fat molecule"

The extent of the addition is controllable to produce the desired balance of saturated : unsaturated sites on product molecules.

- The catalytic hydrogenation of vegetable oils forms compounds with the properties of animal fats.

- This conversion of liquid oils ———> solid fats is called "hardening" and it forms the basis for the very important margarine industry.

Can you now see how "softness" or "spreadability" of a margarine is related to the extent of the hardening (hydrogenation) process?

Soaps and detergents

- The relative cheapness of animal fats and some vegetable oils was a primary reason for their use originally in soap making by *saponification*. (Latin *sapo* = soap).

- Industrial production of soaps involves the alkaline hydrolysis of fats or oils with hot $NaOH(aq)$ and the soaps produced are the sodium salts of the fatty acids present in the esters found in the fats or oils. e.g.

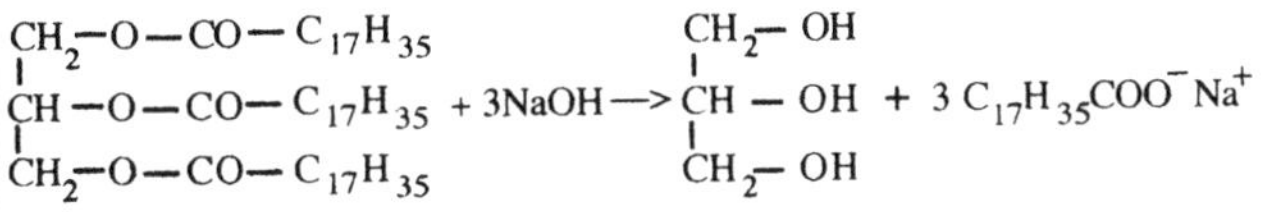

$$\begin{array}{l} CH_2-O-CO-C_{17}H_{35} \\ CH-O-CO-C_{17}H_{35} \\ CH_2-O-CO-C_{17}H_{35} \end{array} + 3NaOH \longrightarrow \begin{array}{l} CH_2-OH \\ CH-OH \\ CH_2-OH \end{array} + 3\ C_{17}H_{35}COO^-Na^+$$

tristearin (glyceryl stearate)   glycerol   sodium stearate

- The addition of sodium stearate to water produces sodium ions and stearate ions in solution. ～～O⁻

stearate ion (representation)

- Stearate ions have a hydrophilic ('water-loving') "head" and a hydrophobic ('water-hating') "tail".

- The cleansing action of a soap is based on the ability of the soap "tails" to dissolve in "oil" while the soap "heads" remain in the water.

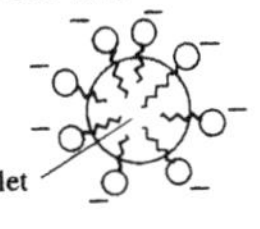

"oil" droplet

- Emulsified oil droplets (called micelles) have no tendency to come together due to repulsive forces which exist between the negatively charged micelles.

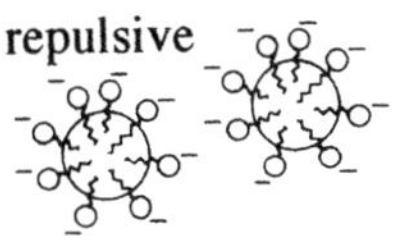

- Metal ions (other than Na^+) in soaps, give soaps with different properties e.g. using hot $KOH(aq)$ produces semi-solid or "soft soaps" more suited for use in liquid soap dispensers or in shampoos.

- Most other metal soaps are insoluble in water but a few specialised uses can be found for these soaps e.g. chemical lubricants or stabilisers in polymers.

- In hard water areas (due to Ca^{2+} and Mg^{2+} ions in the water supplies), soap use produces poor lathering with scum formation and, consequently, a poor overall cleansing action!

- Scum is $(C_{17}H_{35}COO^-)_2Ca^{2+}$, calcium stearate, and/or $(C_{17}H_{35}COO^-)_2Mg^{2+}$, magnesium stearate, both highly insoluble salts which settle out on the items being washed.

- Soap "tails" held within insoluble scum are thus not free to dissolve in oily or greasy deposits and so form the emulsified micelles.

- Use of water softeners offers a solution (expensive!) but even in soft water areas, due to Ca^{2+} and Mg^{2+} ions present in dirt, soil and general stains on clothes, some scum still forms. These, and also soap particles not washed away at the rinsing stage, can accumulate in the fibres of clothes fabrics eventually making them feel less comfortable to the wearer!

- The development of washing materials completely unassociated with natural fats and oils has given rise to huge detergents industries worldwide.

- Early detergents, including sodium alkylbenzenene sulphonates, had a better cleansing action

$$CH_3\text{-}CH\text{-}CH_2\text{-}CH\text{-}CH_2\text{-}CH\text{-}CH_2\text{-}\underset{\underset{H}{|}}{\overset{\overset{CH_3}{|}}{C}}\text{-}\hspace{-2pt}\bigcirc\hspace{-2pt}\text{-}SO_3^-Na^+$$

with CH₃ groups shown: CH_3, CH_3, CH_3, CH_3

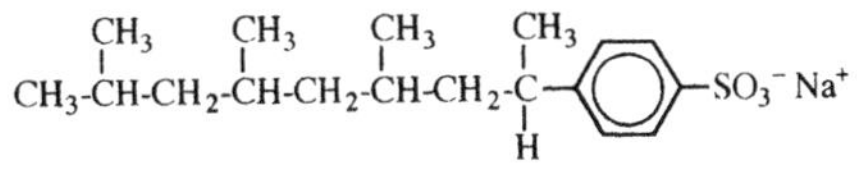

a sodium alkylbenzenesulphonate

than soaps and since their calcium and magnesium salts are soluble, they produced no scum formation.

- However, they were resistant to biodegradation and created undesirable foams in the waste waters to which they were discharged!

- These problems were found to relate to the branched-hydrocarbon "tail" of the detergent and are overcome by replacement of the branched portion with a straight-chain hydrocarbon "tail". ～～⬡⁻Na⁺

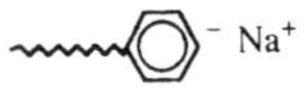

a representation of a detergent

Proteins

- Protein formation in plants and animals cannot take place without absorption of nitrogen or nitrogen compounds.

- Discovery of the technique of paper chromatography led to the separation and identification of amino acids – the "building blocks of proteins" – in the hydrolysis products (hydrolysates) of all proteins!

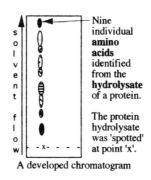

Nine individual **amino acids** identified from the **hydrolysate** of a protein.

The protein hydrolysate was 'spotted' at point 'x'.

A developed chromatogram

- Representations may be used for an amino acid. e.g.

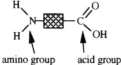

amino group   acid group

represents the other atoms in the molecule

- Of the twenty amino acids commonly found in proteins, a majority have both functional groups bonded to the same carbon atom. e.g.

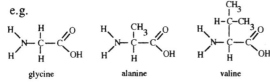

glycine   alanine   valine

- Proteins are condensation polymers of high molecular mass with large numbers of amino acids bonded by peptide links (–CONH–).
(Different amino acids can be shown using different shaded block centres in the model representations).

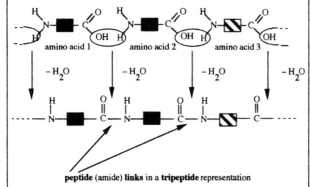

peptide (amide) **links** in a **tripeptide** representation

- Fibrous proteins have linear molecules (*collagen* in muscles and *keratin* in nails and hair).

- Since both $C^{\partial +} = O^{\partial -}$ and $N^{\partial -} – H^{\partial +}$ groups are polar, hydrogen bonding takes place between polypeptide chains forming three-dimensional arrangements often described as the secondary protein structure.

- Some polypeptide strands are also linked by –S–S– bonds or "bridges" by oxidation of –SH groups.

- Intertwining and spiralling of polypeptide chains forms the basis of the more complicated globular protein three-dimensional structures e.g. *casein* in milk and *albumen* in egg white.

Enzyme action

- During digestion, enzymes catalyse the hydrolysis of insoluble proteins in foods to amino acids. The smaller amino acids are then absorbed by the bloodstream and circulated to the various parts of the body.

- Proteins specific to a body's needs e.g. fibrous proteins for tissue, are built up from the amino acids released.

- Body cells cannot make all the amino acids required for body proteins and the body must obtain these so-called "essential amino acids" from proteins in food.

- Hydrolysis of food proteins and condensation of amino acids by body cells can be simplified as:

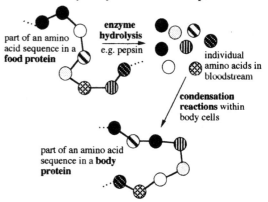

part of an amino acid sequence in a **food protein**

enzyme hydrolysis e.g. pepsin

individual amino acids in bloodstream

condensation reactions within body cells

part of an amino acid sequence in a **body protein**

- Enzyme molecules have specific shapes which match the shape of the proteins with which they react. The expression "lock and key" is often used for enzyme reactions which are "specific" i.e. for catalysing one particular reaction or type of reaction.

Stage 1   Protein molecule approaches the enzyme surface.

Surface contours can adsorb the protein.

surface of the enzyme

Stage 2   Protein molecule is adsorbed at the enzyme surface i.e. the "**key**" fits the "**lock**".

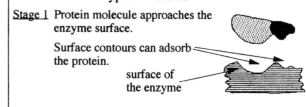

Stage 3   Following hydrolysis, amino acid molecules leave the enzyme surface.

amino acids

the enzyme surface is unaltered

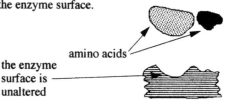

- Destruction of the secondary protein structure as a result of a change in temperature or a change in pH during reaction is known as "denaturing" of the protein i.e. there is a loss of biological activity.

- Enzymes are globular proteins which function efficiently only within narrow pH and temperature ranges i.e. optimum conditions exist for enzyme reactions.

A large plastics industry from small molecules!

- Thermosetting polymers – tough, rigid, three-dimensional network structures – impart strength, heat resistance, electrical insulation, etc, to a wide range of products large and small!

- It all starts with synthesis gas, a mixture of CO and H_2, obtained by the steam reforming of either methane or coal.

$$CH_4 + H_2O \longrightarrow CO + 3H_2$$
methane   "1:3 synthesis gas"

- The relative proportions of CO and H_2 in the manufactured synthesis gas depend on the source materials – methane or coal – since carbon and other hydrocarbons present in coal will undergo the steam reforming process to produce different ratios of CO : H_2.

$$C + H_2O \longrightarrow CO + H_2$$
in coal   "1:1 synthesis gas"

- Methanol is made industrially from synthesis gas from a CO : H_2 ratio of 1 : 2

$$CO + 2H_2 \longrightarrow CH_3OH$$

- Methanol undergoes oxidation to form methanal.

$$CH_3OH \longrightarrow HCHO$$

- Methanal can undergo the process condensation polymerisation with other monomers forming thermosetting polymers like urea-formaldehyde resin (formaldehyde being the non-systematic name for methanal) and here as in Bakelite™ – phenol-formaldehyde resin.

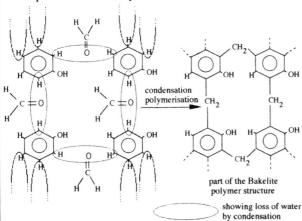

part of the Bakelite polymer structure

showing loss of water by condensation

- Thermosets (thermosetting polymers) like Bakelite™ do **not** soften on heating.

Polyesters and GRP

- Many polymers, including polyesters, are made from monomers with two functional groups per molecule.

- Polyesters form by condensation polymerisation and they soften on heating (thermoplastic).

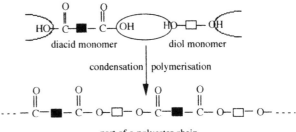

diacid monomer   diol monomer

condensation polymerisation

part of a polyester chain

Note the structure of the ester functional group linking the polyester chain. $-\overset{\displaystyle O}{\overset{\|}{C}}-O-$

- Polyesters with linear structures – like Terylene™ – are manufactured for use as textile fibres.

monomer 1 (benzene-1,4-dicarboxylic acid)   monomer 2 (ethane-1,2-diol)

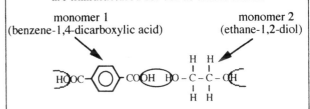

Condensation polymerisation produces long chains of linear polymers suitable for spinning into fibres.

polymer repeating unit

representation of fibre arrangement in linear polyester

- Polymeric esters are also manufactured as polyester resins which, on setting (curing), have strong, rigid, three-dimensional structures.

- Resin kits contain a fairly viscous linear unsaturated polyester dissolved in styrene. The addition of a catalyst establishes cross-links between the styrene and the C = C bonds in the unsaturated polyester.

Representation of the strong, cross-linked, 3-dimensional structure in cured polyester resin.

GRP – glass reinforced plastic – is a mixture of glass fibre with polyester resin. It is used to manufacture many hard-wearing materials including car body panels.

- The sails of modern yachts are made from polyester while the hulls and much of the superstructures are made from a range of tough, hard-wearing, weather resistant, thermosetting polymers.

Polyamides

- The first polyamide (a condensation polymer) was nylon-6,6 where the two different monomer molecules each have six carbon atoms – one is a *di*amine (first digit); the other is a *di*carboxylic acid (second digit).

monomer 1   monomer 2   monomer 1

$+ NH_2(CH_2)_6NH_2 + HOOC(CH_2)_4COOH + NH_2(CH_2)_6NH_2 +$

↓

$\cdots -NH-(CH_2)_6-NH-\overset{O}{\overset{||}{C}}-(CH_2)_4-\overset{O}{\overset{||}{C}}-NH-(CH_2)_6-NH- \cdots$

part of the very large nylon–6,6 molecule

- Commercial nylon production uses the *diacid chloride* monomer - not the *diacid*!

Can you see why hydrogen chloride is lost during the condensation reaction and not water?

- Preparation of a polyamide from one monomer with two functional groups is also possible.

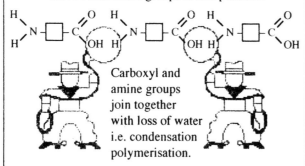

Carboxyl and amine groups join together with loss of water i.e. condensation polymerisation.

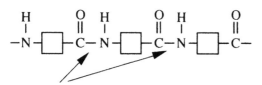

The –CONH– groups are known as amide links.

- $NH_2(CH_2)_5COOH$ used as the only monomer in condensation polymerisation produces Nylon-6.

- Polyamide strands are strongly hydrogen bonded to each other via the $C^{\partial+} = O^{\partial-}$ and $N^{\partial-}- H^{\partial+}$ sites on adjacent polymer chains giving great strength to nylon (polyamide) fibres which is further increased by stretching them strongly during processing.

- Nylons (polyamides) can be produced in batch processes which result in large, solid "blocks" of the condensation polymers.

Remember, water is eliminated in the condensation polymerisation process!

- Nylons can be moulded and/or worked by machinery to produce items as tough as the many metals which they replace. Polymers which possess the properties which allow them to be machined are called "engineering plastics".

Plastics from ethene

- Many plastics are made from ethene obtained from the catalytic cracking of oil fractions.

- Polyethenes are made by addition polymerisation of ethene to form polymer chains of various types and molecular masses.

ethene monomers → part of a polyethene chain

- LDPE (low density polyethene), made in a high pressure process, is made of long branched alkane chains and is more flexible than the HDPE (high density polyethene) which is made in a low pressure process and results in a highly crystalline, rigid polymer of mainly unbranched alkane chains.

- The different properties of LDPE and HDPE are responsible for a wide range of "polyethene goods".

- Polychloroethene (PVC) and polytetrafluoroethene (PTFE) are other well known addition polymers made from unsaturated monomer molecules.

chloroethene monomers → part of a polychloroethene chain

tetrafluoroethene monomers → part of a polytetrafluoroethene chain

A substituted alkene monomer with structural formula as shown opposite, will form an addition polymer chain with structure– and repeating unit–

Halogenoalkanes

- The halogenoalkanes have Cl, Br or I atoms in place of H atoms on alkane molecules and are very important starting materials for lab chemists synthesising a wide range of organic compounds.

- Chloroethane, CH_3CH_2Cl, 'freezes' skin and has uses as a local anaesthetic in minor hospital "ops". It has been of great commercial importance in the production of a widely-used "anti-knock" agent.

$4C_2H_5Cl + Pb + 4Na \longrightarrow (C_2H_5)_4Pb + 4NaCl$
(lead-sodium alloy)   tetraethyl-lead

- Progressive substitution of methane by Cl_2 gives:

$CH_3Cl \longrightarrow CH_2Cl_2 \longrightarrow CHCl_3 \longrightarrow CCl_4$

chloromethane (very toxic) | dichloromethane (non-toxic solvent) | trichloromethane (chloroform - first anaesthetic*) | tetrachloromethane (dry cleaning fluid* no longer in use)

The discovery of the carcinogenic properties of $CHCl_3$ and CCl_4 brought the above uses* to an immediate end but both compounds continued to be employed in the manufacture of chlorofluorocarbons (CFCs).

CFCs - their rise and fall?

- Chlorofluoromethanes like CCl_2F_2 and CCl_3F (called freons or CFCs) appeared to possess the ideal set of properties – non-flammable, non-toxic, chemically inert, very low boiling points – for safe use as coolants (refrigerants) and as gas propellants for foams and aerosols.

- Preparation of dichlorodifluoromethane is possible from the hazardous tetrachloromethane:

$$CCl_4 + 2HF \longrightarrow CCl_2F_2 + 2HCl$$

- In recent years, however, a major environmental problem, caused by large scale, world-wide CFC usage, has emerged!

- Due to their high volatilities and chemical inertness, CFCs are being carried high into the stratosphere (the upper layers of the earth's atmosphere).

- Intense ultraviolet radiation from the sun breaks the CFC molecules into *radicals* (very reactive species) which react with the ozone, O_3, in the stratosphere.

- Ozone is made by a photochemical process in the upper atmosphere and it is now known that it can shield the earth's surface from much of the ultra violet radiation from outer space.

- CFC molecules are believed to participate in the destruction of the ozone layer in the upper layers of the atmosphere through steps such as these:

$$CCl_2F_2 \xrightarrow{UV} CClF_2{\bullet} + Cl{\bullet}$$
$$Cl{\bullet} + O_3 \longrightarrow ClO{\bullet} + O_2$$
$$ClO{\bullet} + O_3 \longrightarrow Cl{\bullet} + 2O_2$$

- CFCs also absorb heat more strongly than carbon dioxide and so they too contribute (as greenhouse gases) to the "global warming" problem.

Compounds with hydrogen present e.g. chlorodifluoromethane, $CHClF_2$, are known to decompose in lower regions of the atmosphere and are thought to have a lesser effect on "upper ozone" destruction than other CFCs. However, they too contribute to global warming and air pollution, so the CFC problems remain to be resolved!

Some interesting developments in polymer chemistry

Heard about the plastic sheeting for market gardeners and farmers which not only helps to retain warmth and moisture in soil beneath covered plants but decomposes slowly when moist, releasing fertilizing ammonia into the soil? Or, the 100% plastic aeroplane to allow for higher speed, longer range and lower fuel consumption? Yes - such polymers have been designed by chemists for these particular applications!

- Many years of research by chemists in the UK led to the development of the biodegradable polymer, BIOPOL™, a thermoplastic polymer produced by bacterial fermentation.

- Plastics, such as polyethenes, are generally quite resistant to degradation but this can be achieved by making alterations to the polymer structure during the production stage by introducing "sites" capable of being "attacked" by either bacteria or by light as in the case of carbonyl groups (photodegradation).

- Polymerisation of the monomer with the structure shown opposite can produce a plastic capable of vibrating at high frequency when it receives an electric impulse. Could this be the "tweeter" material of future loudspeakers?

Can you see why this polymer is named systematically as poly(1,1-difluoroethene)?

- Ethyne (*acetylene*) polymerises to give a polyene with the chain structure–

$$--CH = CH - CH = CH - CH = CH --$$

This polymer, called polyethyne (*polyacetylene*), may be "doped" with traces of certain metals or metal compounds to raise its electrical conducting properties (delocalised electrons along the polymer chain). The polymer material can act like a metal but it is, of course, - because of its composition - much lighter in weight!

- Some photocopier drums use the photoconducting property of a layer of the addition polymer – poly(vinylcarbazole).

vinyl carbazole monomer

- Kevlar™, an aromatic polyamide, is one of the strongest plastics made to date. Its rigid, linear

Kevlar repeating unit

molecules are parallel (hydrogen bonded) and a spinning process during manufacturing, forming stacked "sheets" of molecules in a near perfect crystal, gives Kevlar its exceptional properties. Kevlar surpasses steel wire in strength and has been used for bullet-proof vests, underwater cables, wind-surfing sails and aeroplane body parts.

- Polyvinyl esters undergo ester exchange reactions with methanol to form polyvinyl alcohol (PVA).

poly(vinylethanoate) $\xrightarrow[(-CH_3COOCH_3)]{CH_3OH}$ poly(vinyl alcohol)

- Various PVA "grades" are manufactured where the extent of their solubility depends on the number of unhydrolysed ethanoate groups remaining.

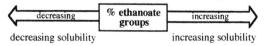

decreasing ← | % ethanoate groups | → increasing

decreasing solubility   increasing solubility

- PVA is used, as packaging film for foods, textiles and stationery, in adhesives, in the paper industry and in the coloured polymer gel SLIME™ sold in toyshops. PVA foams make ideal plastic sponges!

UNIT 3   Chemical Reactions

Chemical equilibrium

- Reversible reactions attain a state of dynamic equilibrium within a closed system when the rates of forward and backward reactions are equal.

- At equilibrium, the concentrations of reactant(s) and product(s) remain constant though not necessarily equal.

Do you understand what these statements are saying?

- When a system reaches equilibrium, both reactions appear to have "stopped" as concentrations of the reactant(s) and product(s) remain unchanged.

- In fact, the forward and backward reactions are still taking place and the rate of conversion of the reactant(s) to product(s) is the same as the rate of conversion of product(s) to reactant(s) i.e. concentrations of reactant(s) and product(s) remain constant.

- The sign $\rightleftharpoons$ for reversible reactions is used to show that a system is in equilibrium.

- Many chemical reactions are reversible.

Factors which can change the position of equilibrium

- Systems which are in equilibrium can have the position of equilibrium changed by affecting either the rate of the forward or the backward reaction.

- Factors which can bring about these changes are concentration, temperature and pressure. (Pressure changes only affect gaseous systems.)

- A useful observation made about all systems in equilibrium states that: if a system in equilibrium is subjected to a change, e.g. of concentration, temperature or pressure, the position of the equilibrium will tend to move in such a way as to oppose the change being made on the system.

Changes in concentration

- [ ] = "concentration of" a reactant or product.

- Increase in concentration of reactant(s) or decrease in concentration of product(s) always increases the rate of the forward reaction, forming more product(s) i.e. the equilibrium moves to the right.

- Increase in concentration of product(s) or decrease in concentration of reactant(s) always increases the rate of the backward reaction, forming more reactant(s) i.e. the equilibrium moves to the left.

  e.g. consider the system $A + B \rightleftharpoons C$

  Increase in [A] or [B] moves equilibrium $\longrightarrow$
  Increase in [C] moves equilibrium $\longleftarrow$
  Decrease in [A] or [B] moves equilibrium $\longleftarrow$
  Decrease in [C] moves equilibrium $\longrightarrow$

Following equilibrium changes

Changes in position of chemical equilibrium can be followed by observation of changes in colour or pH.

- $Cr_2O_7^{2-}(aq) + OH^-(aq) \rightleftharpoons 2CrO_4^{2-}(aq) + H^+(aq)$
  orange   yellow

  Adding a few drops of alkali to the equilibrium mixture increases $[OH^-(aq)]$ and forms a deeper yellow colour i.e. the equilibrium moves to the right, momentarily favouring the forward reaction.

  Can you see that addition of a few drops of dilute acid would form a deeper orange colour?

- $CH_3COOH(aq) \rightleftharpoons CH_3COO^-(aq) + H^+(aq)$

  Adding ethanoate ions to the equilibrium mixture lowers the pH i.e. the equilibrium moves to the left, momentarily favouring the backward reaction.

- $NH_3(aq) + H_2O(l) \rightleftharpoons NH_4^+(aq) + OH^-(aq)$

  Adding ammonium ions to the equilibrium mixture lowers the pH i.e. the equilibrium moves to the left, momentarily favouring the backward reaction.

- $Fe^{3+}(aq) + CNS^-(aq) \rightleftharpoons FeCNS^{2+}(aq)$
  pale yellow   colourless   blood-red

  Increase in $[Fe^{3+}]$ moves equilibrium $\longrightarrow$
  Increase in $[CNS^-]$ moves equilibrium $\longrightarrow$

Can you see that a deeper blood-red colour would appear?

Can you also see that the removal of either $Fe^{3+}(aq)$ or $CNS^-(aq)$ would result in a loss of blood-red colour?

Changes in temperature

- Decrease in temperature will make a system, which is in equilibrium, always move in the direction of the exothermic reaction i.e. the system is opposing a decrease in temperature by heating up i.e. the reaction which has $-\Delta H$ will be favoured momentarily.

- Increase in temperature will make a system, which is in equilibrium, always move in the direction of the endothermic reaction i.e. the system is opposing an increase in temperature by cooling down, and so the reaction which has $+\Delta H$ will be favoured momentarily.

  e.g. consider the system $P \rightleftharpoons Q + R$ ΔH +ve
  (Note: The ΔH value refers to the forward reaction.)

  Increase in temperature moves equilibrium $\longrightarrow$
  Decrease in temperature moves equilibrium $\longleftarrow$
  e.g.

     ΔH +ve
  pale yellow   brown

Increase in temperature moves the equilibrium to the right forming a darker brown mixture, while a decrease in temperature moves the equilibrium to the left forming a paler yellow mixture.

Changes in pressure

- Systems in equilibrium which contain gas(es) as either reactant(s) or product(s) can be affected by changes in pressure.

- An increase in number of gas particles in a closed system causes an increase in pressure.
  Similarly, a decrease in number of gas particles causes a decrease in pressure.

- Increase in pressure always moves the equilibrium momentarily in the direction which opposes this effect i.e. favouring the formation of fewer gas particles.

- Decrease in pressure always moves the equilibrium momentarily in the direction which opposes this effect i.e. favouring the formation of more gas particles.

Consider pressure changes in the following:

$$N_2O_4(g) \rightleftharpoons 2NO_2(g)$$
| 1 mol | 2 mol |
| 1 vol | 2 vol |

Increase in total volume to the right.

Increase in pressure moves equilibrium ◄——
Decrease in pressure moves equilibrium ——►

$$2SO_2(g) + O_2(g) \rightleftharpoons 2SO_3(g)$$
| 2 mol | 1 mol | 2 mol |
| 2 vol | 1 vol | 2 vol |

Decrease in total volume to the right.

Increase in pressure moves equilibrium ——►
Decrease in pressure moves equilibrium ◄——

$$C(s) + O_2(g) \rightleftharpoons CO_2(g)$$
| 1 mol | 1 mol | 1 mol |
| – | 1 vol | 1 vol |

There is no change in total volume and so changes in pressure have no effect on the position of equilibrium.

Catalysts and equilibrium

- Catalysts lower activation energy of both forward and backward reactions to the same extent and so they do not affect the position of equilibrium but speed up the rate of attainment of equilibrium.

An important equilibrium!

- Nitrogen and hydrogen combine to form ammonia but after a while the ammonia decomposes as quickly as it is formed i.e. equilibrium is attained.

$$N_2(g) + 3H_2(g) \rightleftharpoons 2NH_3(g) \quad \Delta H \text{ –ve}$$

- Ammonia is highly desirable and of great commercial value but under normal conditions, reaction rate is slow and the yield is very low!

What can be done to ensure that ammonia is formed faster than it decomposes and in greater quantity?

- It would appear that:
  increase in $[N_2]$ or $[H_2]$ moves equilibrium ——►
  decrease in $[NH_3]$ moves equilibrium ——►
  decrease in temperature moves equilibrium ——►
  increase in pressure moves equilibrium ——►

The Haber Process

The German chemist Fritz Haber devised a highly economic and efficient industrial process for ammonia production which prevented attainment of equilibrium in the nitrogen/hydrogen/ammonia reaction.

- To increase the rate of reaction, an iron catalyst is used but this does not alter the yield of NH_3!

- Other catalysts e.g. platinum, may offer greater activity or longer life but would add greatly to raw material costs!

- To make the reaction fast enough to be economic, it is necessary to have a high temperature but, unfortunately, this reduces the product yield!

- A "compromise temperature" of 450–500 °C is chosen to allow a reasonable rate and an acceptable level of ammonia decomposition!

- Yield of ammonia (~15%) can be improved if the pressure of the gas mixture is increased but with this comes the increased risk of explosions and also increased expenditure on pressure piping and even stronger vessels for the ammonia plant!

- A "compromise pressure" of ~200 atmospheres is therefore used!

- Removing liquefied ammonia by cooling the gas mixture formed and recycling of the unreacted gases prevents equilibrium from ever being achieved!

- Modern ammonia plants produce several hundred tonnes per day and are sited close to sources of water, transport, energy and population!

- In practice, industrial operating conditions are always a compromise between many factors!

Equilibrium in water

- Pure water is very slightly ionised and forms an equilibrium mixture of molecules and ions.

$$H_2O(l) \rightleftharpoons H^+(aq) + OH^-(aq)$$
mainly molecules   very few ions

- When some metals react with water – which is neutral – hydrogen is released and the solution becomes alkaline.
  e.g. Na/H_2O reaction

$$2Na(s) \longrightarrow 2Na^+(aq) + 2e^-$$
$$2H^+(aq) + 2e^- \longrightarrow H_2(g)$$

- As the $H^+(aq)$ ions are used up to form $H_2(g)$, the water equilibrium will move to the right. This increases the $[OH^-]$ ions over $[H^+]$ to make the solution alkaline.

- Neutral aqueous solutions can become acidic by either addition of $H^+(aq)$ or removal of $OH^-(aq)$.

- Neutral aqueous solutions can become alkaline by either addition of $OH^-(aq)$ or removal of $H^+(aq)$.

The pH scale

- The pH of an aqueous solution is a measure of the hydrogen ion concentration present.

- In water and neutral solutions, $[H^+] = [OH^-]$

- In acidic solutions, $[H^+] > [OH^-]$

- In alkaline solutions, $[OH^-] > [H^+]$

- Concentrations of hydrogen ions and hydroxide ions in pure water or neutral aqueous solutions are very small and when measured at 25 °C are:

  $[H^+] = 10^{-7}$ mol dm^{-3} and $[OH^-] = 10^{-7}$ mol dm^{-3}

- The ionic product $[H^+][OH^-] = 10^{-14}$ mol^2 dm^{-6}

You do not have to be a great mathematician to see how pH values are obtained knowing either [H$^+$] or [OH$^-$]! Look closely at the negative power values!

- $pH = - \lg [H^+]$, so in pure water or neutral solution,
  $pH = - \lg [10^{-7}]$
  $= - (-7)$
  $= 7$

Would you be surprised to know that the pH of an aqueous solution of [H$^+$] = 10^{-5} mol dm^{-3} is 5?

Could you calculate the pH of 0.1 mol dm^{-3} HCl(aq) and the pH of 0.1 mol dm^{-3} NaOH(aq)?

  In 0.1 mol dm^{-3} HCl(aq), $[H^+] = 10^{-1}$ mol dm^{-3}
  $pH = - \lg[H^+] = - \lg[10^{-1}] = - (-1) = 1$

In the case of the 0.1 mol dm^{-3} NaOH(aq), the [OH$^-$] should first be stated in a suitable form:

  In 0.1 mol dm^{-3} NaOH(aq), $[OH^-] = 10^{-1}$ mol dm^{-3}

Remember, the ionic product links [H$^+$] and [OH$^-$].

  $[H^+][OH^-] = 10^{-14}$ mol^2 dm^{-6}
  $=> [H^+] = 10^{-14}/[OH^-] = 10^{-14}/10^{-1} = 10^{-13}$ mol dm^{-3}
  $=> pH = - \lg[H^+] = - \lg[10^{-13}] = - (-13) = 13$

- 1 mol dm^{-3} HCl(aq) and 1 mol dm^{-3} NaOH(aq) have pH values of 0 and 14, respectively.
  So, concentrations > 1 mol dm^{-3} for HCl(aq) and NaOH(aq) – within limits of solubility – give values < zero and > 14, respectively.
  Try to work out some of these for yourself!

- *Caution! Watch the formulae of some acids!*
  0.1 mol dm^{-3} H$_2$SO$_4$(aq) has $[H^+] = 0.2$ mol dm^{-3}
  0.1 mol dm^{-3} H$_3$PO$_4$(aq) has $[H^+] = 0.3$ mol dm^{-3}

- The pH scale is in fact a continuous scale and has values from < zero (– ve values) to >14.

- pH   1   2   3   4   5   6   **7**   8   9   10 11 12 13 **14**
  $[H^+]$ **10^{-1}** <———— **10^{-7}** ————> **10^{-14}**

      increasing acidity   **neutral**   increasing alkalinity

- A tenfold dilution in [H$^+$] results in an increase in pH value of 1!

Strong and weak acids

- "Strong" and "weak" when applied to acids do not mean the same as concentrated and dilute!

- A strong acid is one which is fully ionised in solution e.g. HCl(aq), HNO$_3$(aq), H$_2$SO$_4$(aq) and H$_3$PO$_4$(aq).

- No acid molecules are present as these are completely dissociated into ions.
  e.g.   HCl(aq) $\longrightarrow$ H$^+$(aq) + Cl$^-$(aq)
        H$_2$SO$_4$(aq) $\longrightarrow$ 2H$^+$(aq) + SO$_4^{2-}$(aq)

- A weak acid is one which is partially ionised in solution e.g H$_2$CO$_3$(aq) – carbonic acid and H$_2$SO$_3$(aq) – sulphurous acid.
       CO$_2$(g) + H$_2$O(l) $\rightleftharpoons$ 2H$^+$(aq) + CO$_3^{2-}$(aq)
       SO$_2$(g) + H$_2$O(l) $\rightleftharpoons$ 2H$^+$(aq) + SO$_3^{2-}$(aq)

  Both carbonic and sulphurous acids are present in "acid rain" which attacks iron structures, buildings and limestone statues (containing CaCO$_3$/MgCO$_3$).

  i.e.   metal + acid $\longrightarrow$ salt + hydrogen

  and,   metal + acid $\longrightarrow$ salt + water + carbon
       carbonate   dioxide

- All carboxylic acids are weak.
  i.e. RCOOH(aq) $\rightleftharpoons$ RCOO$^-$(aq) + H$^+$(aq)

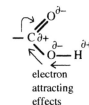

The polarisation of the C=O bond in carboxylic acids has the effect of attracting neighbouring bonding electrons which limits the ionisation of the O–H group and hence limits the formation of hydrogen ions in solution.

- Equimolar solutions of strong and weak acids differ in pH, conductivity and reaction rates but not in stoichiometry of reactions.

	0.1 mol dm^{-3} HCl(aq)	0.1 mol dm^{-3} CH$_3$COOH
pH	1	~3
Conductivity	high	low
Reaction rate (Mg or CaCO$_3$ in excess with equal volumes of acids)	fast	slow
Volume of gases evolved	<—— same amount——>	
Volume 0.1 mol dm^{-3} NaOH(aq) required for neutralisation	<—— same amount——>	

Strong and weak acids have the same combining ratios (stoichiometry) of reactants in reactions. (See above table)
e.g. with ethanoic acid solution (a weak acid):
CH$_3$COOH(aq) $\rightleftharpoons$ CH$_3$COO$^-$(aq) + H$^+$(aq)
mainly undissociated   very few ions
    molecules

As reactions with Mg or CaCO$_3$ or NaOH(aq) proceed and H$^+$(aq) ions are used up, the acid equilibrium moves to the right and continues until all the acid molecules have dissociated to bring about complete reaction with the reagents.

Strong and weak bases

- "Strong" and "weak" when applied to bases do not mean the same as concentrated and dilute!

- A strong base is one which is fully ionised in solution e.g. NaOH(aq) and KOH(aq).

$$NaOH(s) + aq \longrightarrow Na^+(aq) + OH^-(aq)$$
$$KOH(s) + aq \longrightarrow K^+(aq) + OH^-(aq)$$

- A weak base is one which is partially ionised in solution e.g. NH_3(aq) and solutions of some amines.

$$NH_3(g) + H_2O(l) \rightleftharpoons NH_4^+(aq) + OH^-(aq)$$
ammonia   water   ammonium   hydroxide
                     ions   ions

The non-bonding pairs of electrons on the N atoms in NH_3 molecules bond to H atoms in H_2O molecules resulting in formation of OH^-(aq) and NH_4^+(aq) ions. The co-ordinate or dative covalent bond formed to create the NH_4^+(aq) ion is "unusual" in that both electrons being shared to form the bond are donated by one of the atoms! Once formed, this bond is not distinguishable from other H–N bonds in the ion!

pyramidal shape   angular shape   tetrahedral shape   co-ordinate or dative bond

- Aliphatic primary amines are weak bases and react with water producing alkaline solutions.

$$CH_3NH_2(g) + H_2O(l) \rightleftharpoons CH_3NH_3^+(aq) + OH^-(aq)$$
methylamine   water   methylammonium ions   hydroxide ions

$$C_2H_5NH_2(g) + H_2O(l) \rightleftharpoons C_2H_5NH_3^+(aq) + OH^-(aq)$$
ethylamine   water   ethylammonium ions   hydroxide ions

- Equimolar solutions of strong and weak bases differ in pH and conductivity but not in stoichiometry of reactions.

	0.1 mol dm⁻³ NaOH(aq)	0.1 mol dm⁻³ NH₃(aq)
pH	14	~11
Conductivity	high	low
Volume 0.1 mol dm⁻³ HCl(aq) required for neutralisation of equal volumes	← same amount →	

Strong and weak bases have the same combining ratios (stoichiometry) of reactants in reactions. (See above table)
e.g. with ammonia solution (a weak base):

$$NH_3(g) + H_2O(l) \rightleftharpoons NH_4^+(aq) + OH^-(aq)$$
mainly undissociated molecules   very few ions

As reaction with HCl(aq) proceeds and OH^-(aq) ions are used up to form water, the above equilibrium moves to the right and continues until all the ammonia molecules have been ionised to bring about complete reaction with the acid.

Estimating pH of solutions

- Concentrations of acidic and basic solutions do not always correspond exactly to 10^{-1}, 10^{-2}, 10^{-3} mol dm⁻³, etc, when it is a simple task to calculate the pH of the acid or alkali.

You can, however, estimate the pH of any solution by finding where the [H⁺] lies between set values.
e.g.
[H⁺] = 0.001 mol dm⁻³ = 10^{-3} mol dm⁻³ => pH = 3.
[H⁺] = 0.0001 mol dm⁻³ = 10^{-4} mol dm⁻³ => pH = 4.
So for [H⁺] between 0.001 mol dm⁻³ and 0.0001 mol dm⁻³, say 0.0005 mol dm⁻³, => pH value is between 3 and 4.

Estimating [H⁺] in a primary amine solution with pH = 11.2 is possible because pH lies between 11 and 12 i.e. [H⁺] of the amine solution is between 10^{-11} and 10^{-12} mol dm⁻³.

pH of salt solutions

These, too, can be estimated from a knowledge of the strong/weak natures of the parent acid and alkali.

- Not all salt solutions are neutral i.e. pH = 7.

- A solution of a salt prepared from a strong acid and a strong alkali has pH = 7 e.g. NaCl(aq).

Consider the species present:
$$NaCl(aq) \longrightarrow Na^+(aq) + Cl^-(aq)$$
and, $$H_2O(l) \rightleftharpoons OH^-(aq) + H^+(aq)$$

NaOH(aq) is a strong alkali and HCl(aq) is a strong acid and so no reaction takes place between the "salt ions" and the water. Therefore, [H⁺] = [OH⁻] and pH = 7.

- A solution of a salt prepared from a strong acid and a weak alkali has pH < 7 e.g. NH_4Cl(aq).

Consider the species present:
$$NH_4Cl(aq) \longrightarrow NH_4^+(aq) + Cl^-(aq)$$
and, $$H_2O(l) \rightleftharpoons OH^-(aq) + H^+(aq)$$

A reaction takes place to upset the water equilibrium! $$NH_3(aq) + H_2O(l)$$

Ammonium hydroxide is a weak alkali and ammonium ions and hydroxide ions react to establish an equilibrium with ammonia and water molecules. This results in an excess of H⁺(aq) over OH⁻(aq) as the water equilibrium moves to the right producing more ions.
i.e. [H⁺] > [OH⁻] and pH < 7.

- A solution of a salt prepared from a weak acid and a strong alkali has pH > 7 e.g. CH_3COONa(aq) or soap solutions.

Consider the species present in aqueous sodium ethanoate:
$$CH_3COONa(aq) \longrightarrow CH_3COO^-(aq) + Na^+(aq)$$
and, $$H_2O(l) \rightleftharpoons H^+(aq) + OH^-(aq)$$

A reaction takes place to upset the water equilibrium! $$CH_3COOH(aq)$$

Ethanoic acid is a weak acid and ethanoate ions and hydrogen ions react to establish an equilibrium with ethanoic acid and water molecules. This results in an excess of OH⁻(aq) over H⁺(aq) as the water equilibrium moves to the right producing more ions.
i.e. [H⁺] < [OH⁻] and pH > 7.

Redox reactions

- Oxidation involves the loss of electrons.
  e.g. $Mg(s) \longrightarrow Mg^{2+}(aq) + 2e^-$
  (Simple ion-electron equation showing the oxidation of Mg atoms to Mg^{2+} ions.)

- Reduction involves the gain of electrons.
  e.g. $Ag^+(aq) + e^- \longrightarrow Ag(s)$
  (Simple ion-electron equation showing the reduction of Ag^+ ions to Ag atoms.)

- Oxidation cannot take place without reduction and the overall reaction is called a redox reaction.
  e.g. $Mg(s) + 2Ag^+(aq) \longrightarrow Mg^{2+}(aq) + 2Ag(s)$
  (The redox equation with no "spectator ions" present.)

- Complex ion-electron equations may involve $H^+(aq)$ and $H_2O(l)$ in addition to main reactant and product species.
  e.g. $MnO_4^-(aq) + 8H^+(aq) + 5e^- \longrightarrow Mn^{2+}(aq) + 4H_2O(l)$

- Complex ion-electron equations, for either oxidation or reduction, are written by following a "set of rules":

---

1. Balance for the main element symbol.

2. Add sufficient $H_2O(l)$ to balance for any O present in the formulae.

3. Add sufficient $H^+(aq)$ to balance the H present in the formulae.

4. Add sufficient e^- to balance the charge.

---

e.g. To write the balanced ion-electron equation for the change $MnO_4^-(aq) \longrightarrow Mn^{2+}(aq)$.

1. The main element symbol, Mn, **is** balanced.

2. Four $H_2O(l)$ are needed on the RHS to balance the four O in MnO_4^-:

$\Rightarrow MnO_4^-(aq) \longrightarrow Mn^{2+}(aq) + 4H_2O(l)$

3. This has introduced eight H on the RHS, so eight $H^+(aq)$ must be added to the LHS:

$\Rightarrow MnO_4^-(aq) + 8H^+(aq) \longrightarrow Mn^{2+}(aq) + 4H_2O(l)$

4. Charge on LHS (reactants) = $(-1 + 8)$ = +7
   Charge on RHS (products) = +2
   Add 5 e^- to LHS to equalise the charge at +2
   $\Rightarrow$ Final balanced ion-electron equation:

$MnO_4^-(aq) + 8H^+(aq) + 5e^- \longrightarrow Mn^{2+}(aq) + 4H_2O(l)$

Browsing time again!
Just a couple of ion-electron
equation worked examples!
Can you follow the stages
taken in the "set of rules"?

$SO_3^{2-}(aq) \longrightarrow SO_4^{2-}(aq)$

$SO_3^{2-}(aq) + H_2O(l) \longrightarrow SO_4^{2-}(aq)$

$SO_3^{2-}(aq) + H_2O(l) \longrightarrow SO_4^{2-}(aq) + 2H^+(aq)$

$SO_3^{2-}(aq) + H_2O(l) \longrightarrow SO_4^{2-}(aq) + 2H^+(aq) + 2e^-$

$IO_3^-(aq) \longrightarrow I_2(s)$

$2IO_3^-(aq) \longrightarrow I_2(s)$

$2IO_3^-(aq) \longrightarrow I_2(s) + 6H_2O(l)$

$2IO_3^-(aq) + 12H^+(aq) \longrightarrow I_2(s) + 6H_2O(l)$

$2IO_3^-(aq) + 12H^+(aq) + 10e^- \longrightarrow I_2(s) + 6H_2O(l)$

Balanced redox equations

- Combine oxidation ion-electron equations with reduction ion-electron equations to form redox equations by balancing the number of electrons "lost" and "gained" by the reaction species.

Example: $Cr_2O_7^{2-}/Fe^{2+}$ system (state symbols omitted)

$Fe^{2+} \longrightarrow Fe^{3+} + e^-$ (oxidation)
$Cr_2O_7^{2-} + 14H^+ + 6e^- \longrightarrow 2Cr^{3+} + 7H_2O$ (reduction)

Balance the number of electrons in the oxidation and reduction ion-electron equations and add!

$6Fe^{2+} \longrightarrow 6Fe^{3+} + \cancel{6e^-}$
$Cr_2O_7^{2-} + 14H^+ + \cancel{6e^-} \longrightarrow 2Cr^{3+} + 7H_2O$

Adding the two ion-electron equations gives the overall redox reaction equation:

$Cr_2O_7^{2-} + 14H^+ + 6Fe^{2+} \longrightarrow 2Cr^{3+} + 6Fe^{3+} + 7H_2O$

Example: SO_3^{2-}/I_2 system (state symbols omitted)

$SO_3^{2-} + H_2O \longrightarrow SO_4^{2-} + 2H^+ + 2e^-$ (oxidation)
$I_2 + 2e^- \longrightarrow 2I^-$ (reduction)

$SO_3^{2-} + I_2 + H_2O \longrightarrow SO_4^{2-} + 2H^+ + 2I^-$

NB. Ion-electron equation electrons are already balanced!

Redox titrations/calculations

Volumetric calculations based on the results from redox titrations are almost a certainty to appear in examination questions or unit assessments and again it is quite clear that many students attempt these calculations very badly or with little confidence!

Redox volumetric calculations are performed in a similar manner to acid /alkali volumetric calculations.

The first essential is to be able to write the balanced redox equation for the system in question.

Necessary ion-electron equations are usually supplied or present in the Data Booklet.

Here is a typical question and three suggested approaches!

24.2 cm³ 0.1 mol dm⁻³ potassium permanganate reacted with exactly 25 cm³ iron(II) sulphate solution. Calculate the concentration of the iron(II) sulphate solution.

The redox reaction is between permanganate and iron(II) ions:

$$MnO_4^-(aq) + 8H^+(aq) + 5e^- \longrightarrow Mn^{2+}(aq) + 4H_2O(l)$$
$$5Fe^{2+}(aq) \longrightarrow 5Fe^{3+}(aq) + 5e^-$$
$$MnO_4^-(aq) + 8H^+(aq) + 5Fe^{2+}(aq) \longrightarrow Mn^{2+}(aq) + 5Fe^{3+}(aq) + 4H_2O(l)$$

Moles MnO_4^- in $KMnO_4$ solution = concentration (mol dm⁻³) × volume (dm³)
= 0.1 × 0.0242
= 0.00242 moles MnO_4^-

From the balanced redox equation, 1 mol MnO_4^- reacts with 5 mol $Fe^{2+}(aq)$
Moles $Fe^{2+}(aq)$ in $FeSO_4(aq)$ solution = 5 × 0.00242
= 0.0121 moles Fe^{2+}

Concentration of iron(II) sulphate solution = moles / volume
= 0.0121/0.025
= 0.484 mol dm⁻³

Or, if you prefer, use the following formula after writing the balanced redox equation:

$$MnO_4^-(aq) + 8H^+(aq) + 5Fe^{2+}(aq) \longrightarrow Mn^{2+}(aq) + 5Fe^{3+}(aq) + 4H_2O(l)$$

$$\frac{V_1 \times M_1}{N_1} = \frac{V_2 \times M_2}{N_2}$$

where V = volumes of reagents
M = concentrations of reagents
N = moles of each reagent in the balanced redox equation

$$\Rightarrow \frac{25 \times M_1}{5} = \frac{24.2 \times 0.1}{1}$$
$$\Rightarrow 25 \times M_1 = 5 \times 24.2 \times 0.1$$
$$\Rightarrow M_1 = \frac{5 \times 24.2 \times 0.1}{25} = 0.484 \text{ mol dm}^{-3}$$

Or, if you are confident with the pair of ion-electron equations but wish to avoid writing the balanced redox equation, use the following formula:

$$V_1 \times M_1 \times P_1 = V_2 \times M_2 \times P_2$$

where V = volumes of reagents; M = concentrations of reagents;
P = moles of electrons lost or gained by 1 mol of reducing or oxidising agent, respectively.

Reducing agent: $Fe^{2+}(aq) \longrightarrow Fe^{3+}(aq) + e^-$ => P = 1
Oxidising agent: $MnO_4^-(aq) + 8H^+(aq) + 5e^- \longrightarrow Mn^{2+}(aq) + 4H_2O(l)$ => P = 5

$$V_1 \times M_1 \times P_1 = V_2 \times M_2 \times P_2$$
$$\Rightarrow 25 \times M_1 \times 1 = 24.2 \times 0.1 \times 5$$
$$\Rightarrow 25 M_1 = 12.1$$
$$\Rightarrow M_1 = 12.1/25 = 0.484 \text{ mol dm}^{-3}$$

Quantitative electrolysis

- During electrolysis, the production of 1 mol of atoms requires n F coulombs where n is the charge on the ion being discharged and F is one Faraday of charge (96500 C).

  e.g.

  $$Na^+(l) + e^- \longrightarrow Na(l)$$

  The charge to produce 1 mol sodium atoms is 1 F or 96500 C.

  e.g.

  $$Al^{3+}(l) + 3e^- \longrightarrow Al(l)$$

  To produce 1 mol of aluminium atoms requires the passage of 3 F or 3 × 96500 C.

- When diatomic, gaseous elements are discharged during electrolysis, then 2 × n F coulombs are required. Remember, too, that negative ions are attracted to, and discharged at, the positive electrode (anode).

  e.g.

  $$2Cl^-(aq) \longrightarrow Cl_2(g) + 2e^-$$

  The charge to produce 1 mol of chlorine molecules is 2 F or 2 × 96500 C.

  and,

  $$2O^{2-}(l) \longrightarrow O_2(g) + 4e^-$$

  The charge to produce 1 mol of oxygen molecules is 4 F or 4 × 96500 C.

- Charge is calculated from current and time.

Q	=	I	×	t
charge		current		time
in coulombs (C)		in amps (A)		in secs (s)

One of the main "student failures" in quantitative electrolysis calculations is the writing of incorrect ion-electron equations for the reactions taking place at the electrodes during the electrolyses.
The Data Booklet is a useful source for most of the ion-electron equations encountered, but remember to reverse a reduction ion-electron equation if you require an oxidation step.

A typical electrolysis calculation

Dilute sulphuric acid is electrolysed using a current of 0.5 A for 32 minutes 10 seconds.
Calculate the mass of hydrogen discharged.

Total charge passed Q = I × t
= 0.5 × [(32 × 60) + 10] C
= 965 C

$$2H^+(aq) + 2e^- \longrightarrow H_2(g)$$
2 mol $\longrightarrow$ 1 mol
2 × 96500 C $\longrightarrow$ 2 g
193000 C discharges 2 g hydrogen
=> 965 C discharges $\frac{2 \times 965}{193000}$ g = 0.01 g

And there's more!

When a current of 1 A was passed through an electrolysis cell for 40 minutes, 0.5 g of a metal was produced. Given the metal is in Group 2 of the Periodic Table, calculate its relative atomic mass.

Since the metal is in Group 2, its metal ion must be M^{2+}.

$$M^{2+} + 2e^- \longrightarrow M$$
2 mol 1 mol
2 × 96500 C
193000 C $\longrightarrow$ 1 mol
Total charge passed Q = I × t
= 1 × (40 × 60) C
= 2400 C
2400 C discharges 0.5 g metal
=> 193000 C discharges $\frac{0.5 \times 193000}{2400}$ g metal
= 40.2 g
1 mol M = 40.2 g
=> Relative Atomic Mass = 40.2

Magnesium is produced industrially by the electrolysis of molten anhydrous magnesium chloride in a cell operating at 2.5×10^5 A. Calculate the time required to produce 1.2 kg of magnesium.

$$Mg^{2+}(l) + 2e^- \longrightarrow Mg(l)$$
2 mol $\longrightarrow$ 1 mol
2 × 96500 C $\longrightarrow$ 24 g
=> 193000 C $\longrightarrow$ 24 g

If 24 g Mg requires 193000 C
=> 1.2 kg requires $\frac{193000 \times 1.2 \times 1000}{24}$
= 9650000 C

Since, Q = I × t
t = Q/I = $\frac{9650000}{250000}$ s
= 38.6 s

ADVICE FILE

"Remember to:

(i) write the ion-electron equation in order to find the theoretical charge required to discharge exactly 1 mol of the product during electrolysis;
(ii) use Q = I × t to find the actual total charge passed in the experiment;
(iii) if necessary, change moles to mass or volume or number of particles if these are requested."

Hess's Law

- The Conservation of Energy when applied to thermochemistry states that energy may be exchanged between a chemical system and its surroundings but the total energy of the system and the surroundings remains constant.

- The total energy is unchanged during a chemical reaction and so this concept has applications in enthalpy change calculations through Hess's Law.

- Hess's Law states that the enthalpy change in a chemical reaction converting reactants into products is the same regardless of the pathway taken provided the initial and final conditions are the same.

- Hess's Law allows chemists to calculate enthalpy changes for processes which are difficult or impossible to obtain by direct experiment e.g. the determination of enthalpies of formation for most compounds.

- Enthalpy of formation is the enthalpy change when 1 mol of a compound is formed from its constituent elements in their normal or standard states.
  (ΔH values are mainly – ve but can be + ve.)
  e.g.
  $$C(s) + 2H_2(g) \longrightarrow CH_4(g) \quad \Delta H = -75 \text{ kJ}$$

Methane is said to be stable with respect to its elements since it is at a lower enthalpy level than the elements, carbon and hydrogen, from which it forms.

and,
$$2C(s) + 2H_2(g) \longrightarrow C_2H_4(g) \quad \Delta H = +52 \text{ kJ}$$

Ethene is said to be unstable with respect to its elements since it is at a higher enthalpy level than the elements, carbon and hydrogen, from which it forms.

- A very simple example to illustrate this is the enthalpy of formation of carbon monoxide.

$$C(s) + \tfrac{1}{2}O_2(g) \longrightarrow CO(g) \quad \Delta H = ?$$

*If you tried to burn carbon in oxygen to form **only** **carbon monoxide**, it would not be possible as a mixture of carbon, carbon monoxide and carbon dioxide would be obtained!*

It is possible, however, to determine by separate experiments, enthalpy changes for the complete combustion of carbon, and for carbon monoxide, and then to apply the principle of Hess's Law to find a value for the enthalpy of formation of carbon monoxide.

Applying Hess's Law

Study the two worked examples dealing with carbon monoxide formation:

> Calculate the enthalpy of formation of carbon monoxide given that the enthalpies of combustion of carbon and carbon monoxide are –394 kJ mol⁻¹ and –284 kJ mol⁻¹, respectively.

Method 1 – flow chart presentation of information

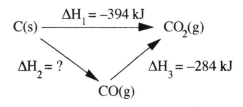

By Hess's Law:
$$\Delta H_1 = \Delta H_2 + \Delta H_3$$
$$\Rightarrow \Delta H_2 = \Delta H_1 - \Delta H_3$$
$$= -394 - (-284)$$
$$= -394 + 284$$

$$\Rightarrow \Delta H_{formation} CO = -110 \text{ kJ mol}^{-1}$$

Method 2 – "adding" a set of balanced equations

Information supplied in question: ΔH
(i) $C(s) + O_2(g) \longrightarrow CO_2(g)$ – 394 kJ
(ii) $CO(g) + \tfrac{1}{2}O_2(g) \longrightarrow CO_2(g)$ – 284 kJ

Applying the information: ΔH
(i) $C(s) + O_2(g) \longrightarrow CO_2(g)$ –394 kJ
Rev (ii) $CO_2(g) \longrightarrow CO(g) + \tfrac{1}{2}O_2(g)$ +284 kJ

Then, by "adding" these two steps:

$C(s) + O_2(g) \longrightarrow \cancel{CO_2(g)}$ –394 kJ
$\cancel{CO_2(g)} \longrightarrow CO(g) + \tfrac{1}{2}O_2(g)$ +284 kJ

$\Rightarrow \quad C(s) + \tfrac{1}{2}O_2(g) \longrightarrow CO(g)$ –110 kJ

(Note: the $\tfrac{1}{2}O_2(g)$ on RHS "cancelled" $\tfrac{1}{2}O_2(g)$ on LHS)

ΔH_f or ΔH_c - they can be the same!

- Enthalpies of formation for most chemical compounds cannot be obtained by experiment although it is possible for a few compounds e.g. the enthalpy of combustion of hydrogen, which can be determined experimentally, is the same as the enthalpy of formation of water.

$$H_2(g) + \tfrac{1}{2}O_2(g) \longrightarrow H_2O(l) \quad \Delta H = -286 \text{ kJ}$$

- The enthalpy of combustion of carbon, which can be determined experimentally, is the same as the enthalpy of formation of carbon dioxide.

$$C(s) + O_2(g) \longrightarrow CO_2(g) \quad \Delta H = -394 \text{ kJ}$$

Enthalpy of formation of methane

Which method suits you?

Method 1

Calculate the enthalpy of formation of methane, CH_4. The enthalpies of combustion of the elements carbon and hydrogen are –394 kJ mol^{-1} and –286 kJ mol^{-1} respectively, while the enthalpy of combustion of methane is –890 kJ mol^{-1}.

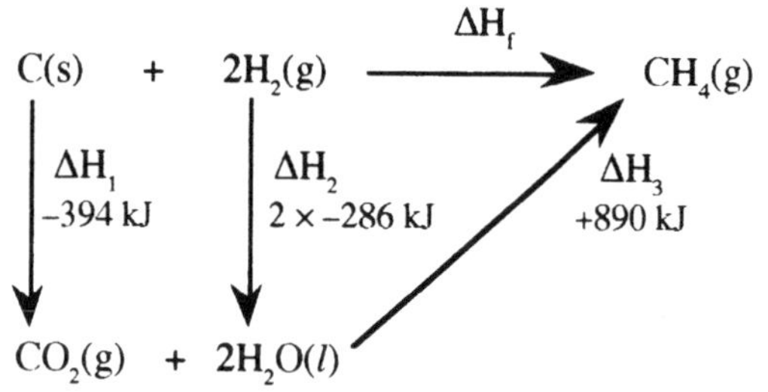

By Hess's Law:

$$\Delta H_f = \Delta H_1 + \Delta H_2 + \Delta H_3$$
$$= -394 + (-572) + 890$$
$$\Delta H_f = -76 \text{ kJ mol}^{-1}$$

Method 2

$C(s) + 2H_2(g) \longrightarrow CH_4(g) \quad \Delta H_f = ?$

Information supplied in question:

	ΔH
$C(s) + O_2(g) \longrightarrow CO_2(g)$	–394 kJ
$H_2(g) + ½O_2(g) \longrightarrow H_2O(l)$	–286 kJ
$CH_4(g) + 2O_2(g) \longrightarrow CO_2(g) + 2H_2O(l)$	–890 kJ

Applying the information:

	ΔH
$C(s) + O_2(g) \longrightarrow CO_2(g)$	–394 kJ
$2H_2(g) + O_2(g) \longrightarrow 2H_2O(l)$	–572 kJ
$CO_2(g) + 2H_2O(l) \longrightarrow CH_4(g) + 2O_2(g)$	+890 kJ

By "adding" these three steps:

$C(s) + \cancel{O_2(g)} \longrightarrow \cancel{CO_2(g)}$	–394 kJ
$2H_2(g) + \cancel{O_2(g)} \longrightarrow \cancel{2H_2O(l)}$	–572 kJ
$\cancel{CO_2(g)} + \cancel{2H_2O(l)} \longrightarrow CH_4(g) + \cancel{2O_2(g)}$	+890 kJ
$C(s) + 2H_2(g) \longrightarrow CH_4(g)$	–76 kJ

Method 3

Use this method if you like to use formulae to help you recall the chemistry!

Calculate enthalpy of formation of CH_4 from the enthalpies of combustion of the elements and the compound.

Apply the following formula:

$$\Delta H_{f\ compound} = \Delta H_{c\ elements} - \Delta H_{c\ compound}$$

$$\Delta H_f CH_4 = \Delta H_c(C + 2H_2) - \Delta H_c CH_4$$
$$= -394 + (-572) - (-890)$$
$$= -76 \text{ kJ mol}^{-1}$$

Remember, the main aim is for you to master any one of the three approaches suggested and for you to feel confident!

Pay particular attention at all times to + ve and – ve signs!

Enthalpy of sublimation

In a number of calculations applying Hess's Law to the chemistry of carbon compounds, you will need to consider the energy required for conversion of solid carbon directly to carbon vapour i.e. carbon in the gaseous state. This is called sublimation enthalpy.

- Enthalpy of sublimation is the enthalpy change when 1 mol of solid is converted into the gaseous state.
  (ΔH is always + ve.)
  e.g. sublimation of carbon
  $C(s) \longrightarrow C(g) \quad \Delta H = +715$ kJ

Bond enthalpies

- Bond enthalpy values relate to the amount of energy absorbed to break 1 mol of covalent bonds or to the energy given out when 1 mol of covalent bonds is made.
  e.g. the Cl – Cl bond enthalpy is 243 kJ mol^{-1} and
  so, $Cl_2(g) \longrightarrow 2Cl(g) \quad \Delta H = +243$ kJ
  and, $2Cl(g) \longrightarrow Cl_2(g) \quad \Delta H = -243$ kJ

Mean bond enthalpies

NB. Information may differ between Data Booklets.

- The same covalent bond between two atoms in different compounds usually exhibits slight differences in the actual values of bond enthalpy due to neighbouring atoms being different!
  e.g. C – H and C – C bonds are found in many millions of molecules and so an **"average"** or **"mean"** bond enthalpy is listed for covalent bonds.

- Data Booklets provide information on mean bond enthalpies.

e.g.

Bond	Mean bond enthalpy / kJ mol^{-1}
C – H	414
C – C	337
C = C	607
C – O	331
C = O	724

- Mean bond enthalpies can be used to calculate
  – other bond enthalpies,
  – enthalpies of formation,
  – enthalpies of sublimation.

ADVICE FILE

"When tackling a mean bond enthalpy calculation, you will find it beneficial to draw out the reactants' and products' structures. Then you can see exactly what is required in terms of the 'bond breaking' and 'bond making' steps. Four worked examples of this type of problem solving question are given on page 47. For further practice, see Leckie & Leckie's Questions in Higher Chemistry."

Mean bond enthalpy calculation

Browse the worked examples showing two methods of tackling the same problem - one may suit you better!

Calculate the bond enthalpy of $C = C$ in ethene given that its enthalpy of formation is +39 kJ mol^{-1}. You may also use the bond enthalpies of $C - H$ and $H - H$ which are 414 kJ mol^{-1} and 436 kJ mol^{-1} respectively, and the enthalpy of sublimation of carbon which is +715 kJ mol^{-1}.

Method 1

$$2C(s) + 2H_2(g) \longrightarrow C_2H_4(g) \quad \Delta H_f = +39 \text{ kJ}$$

Let 'X' be the bond enthalpy of the $C = C$.

Since the carbon atoms in ethene are gaseous, the solid carbon will have to be sublimed.

Bonds broken (ΔH +ve)	Bonds made (ΔH –ve)
$2C(s) \rightarrow 2C(g) = +(2 \times 715)$kJ	$1 \times C = C = -X$
$2 \times H-H = +(2 \times 436)$kJ	$4 \times C-H = -(4 \times 414)$kJ
	$= -1656$ kJ

Total bond breaking	Total bond making
$= +2302$ kJ	$= -1656 - X$ kJ

$$\Delta H_f = \text{sum of bond breaking and bond making}$$
$$+39 = +2302 + (-1656 - X)$$
$$X = +2302 - 1656 - 39$$
$$= 607 \text{ kJ}$$

=> Bond enthalpy of $C = C$ is 607 kJ mol^{-1}

Method 2

Display the information supplied in the question:

$$2C(s) + 2H_2(g) \longrightarrow C_2H_4(g) \quad \Delta H = +39 \text{ kJ}$$
$$H_2(g) \longrightarrow 2H(g) \quad \Delta H = +436 \text{ kJ}$$
$$C(s) \longrightarrow C(g) \quad \Delta H = +715 \text{ kJ}$$

$C - H$ bond enthalpy = 414 kJ mol^{-1}

Start with ethene as reactant by reversing the enthalpy of formation equation and changing the sign!

i.e. $C_2H_4(g) \longrightarrow 2C(s) + 2H_2(g) \quad \Delta H = -39 \text{ kJ}$

Now, consider reaction steps and apply Hess's Law:

	$C(s) \longrightarrow C(g)$	$\Delta H = +715$ kJ
=>	$2C(s) \longrightarrow 2C(g)$	$\Delta H = +1430$ kJ
	$H_2(g) \longrightarrow 2H(g)$	$\Delta H = +436$ kJ
=>	$2H_2(g) \longrightarrow 4H(g)$	$\Delta H = +872$ kJ

*"Adding" the **three highlighted equations**:*

$C_2H_4(g) \rightarrow 2C(s) + 2H_2(g)$	$\Delta H =$	-39 kJ
$2C(s) \rightarrow 2C(g)$	$\Delta H =$	$+1430$ kJ
$2H_2(g) \rightarrow 4H(g)$	$\Delta H =$	$+872$ kJ

$=> C_2H_4(g) \rightarrow 2C(g) + 4H(g) \quad \Delta H = +2263$ kJ

i.e. total energy to break all the bonds = 2263 kJ

Energy to break the four mols $C - H$ bonds in 1 mol ethene requires $4 \times 414 = 1656$ kJ.

So, $2263 - 1656 = 607$ kJ is the energy used to break all the $C = C$ bonds in 1 mol ethene molecules.

=> Bond enthalpy of $C = C$ is 607 kJ mol^{-1}

Enthalpy of formation calculation

Calculate the enthalpy of formation of hydrazine (N_2H_4) using mean bond enthalpies supplied in the Data Booklet. (Use 163 kJ mol^{-1} for N–N bond.)

First, write the equation for the formation:

$$N_2(g) + 2H_2(g) \longrightarrow N_2H_4(g) \quad \Delta H = ?$$

The "bond breaking" and "bond making" may not be obvious from the equation alone but drawing the covalent structures makes the picture clearer!

Bond breaking (ΔH +ve)	Bond making (ΔH –ve)
$1 \times N \equiv N = +949$ kJ	$1 \times N - N = -163$ kJ
$2 \times H-H = +(2 \times 436)$kJ	$4 \times N-H = -(4 \times 387)$ kJ
$= +872$ kJ	$= -1548$ kJ

Total bond	Total bond
breaking $= +1821$ kJ	making $= -1711$ kJ

$$\Delta H_f = \text{sum of bond breaking and bond making}$$
$$= +1821 + (-1711)$$
$$= +110 \text{ kJ } mol^{-1}$$

Hydrazine is unstable with respect to its elements.

Enthalpy of sublimation calculation

The enthalpy of formation of hydrogen sulphide gas is –20 kJ mol^{-1}. Given bond enthalpies of $H - H$ and $S - H$ as 436 kJ mol^{-1} and 338 kJ mol^{-1} respectively, calculate the enthalpy of sublimation of sulphur.

$$S(s) + H_2(g) \longrightarrow H_2S(g) \quad \Delta H = -20 \text{ kJ}$$

Draw structures of reactants and products to see the bond making and bond breaking involved:

Let 'X' be the enthalpy of sublimation of sulphur.

Bond breaking (ΔH +ve)	Bond making (ΔH –ve)
$S(s) \rightarrow S(g) = +X$ kJ	$2 \times S - H = -(2 \times 338)$kJ
$H - H = +436$ kJ	$= -676$ kJ

Total bond	Total
breaking $= X + 436$ kJ	bond making $= -676$ kJ

$\Delta H_f = $ sum of bond breaking and bond making
$$-20 = X + 436 - 676$$
$$X = +676 - 20 - 436$$
$$X = +220 \text{ kJ}$$

Enthalpy of sublimation of sulphur = +220 kJ mol^{-1}

Hess's Law by experiment!

" All these calculations may lead you to think that the chemistry only works out on paper! You can verify Hess's Law for yourself by carrying out a very simple experiment! "

- A solution of sodium chloride may be prepared by either dissolving NaOH(s) directly in HCl(aq) or by dissolving NaOH(s) in water and then adding this NaOH(aq) to HCl(aq).

- These two routes are shown in the flow diagram below:

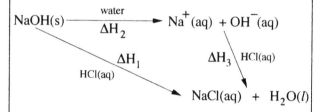

- Enthalpy changes ΔH_1 for route 1, and ΔH_2 and ΔH_3 for route 2, can be calculated using the $H = c\,m\,\Delta T$ expression.

  (Solutions used in the experiments are assumed to have the same specific heat capacity, c, as water.)

- By experiment, $\Delta H_1 = \Delta H_2 + \Delta H_3$

- By experiment, $\Delta T_1 = \Delta T_2 + \Delta T_3$

More useful enthalpy changes

- The first ionisation energy (or enthalpy) is the energy required to remove 1 mol of electrons from 1 mol of gaseous atoms.
  (ΔH is always +ve.)
  e.g. the first ionisation enthalpy of potassium
  $$K(g) \longrightarrow K^+(g) + e^- \quad \Delta H = +420 \text{ kJ}$$

- The second ionisation energy (or enthalpy) is the energy required to remove 1 mol of electrons from 1 mol of positively charged gaseous ions.
  (ΔH is always +ve.)
  e.g. the second ionisation enthalpy of potassium
  $$K^+(g) \longrightarrow K^{2+}(g) + e^- \quad \Delta H = +3070 \text{ kJ}$$

- Mean bond energy (or enthalpy) is the energy associated with 1 mol of chemical bonds.
  Energy is absorbed to break bonds (ΔH +ve) and is released when bonds are made (ΔH –ve).
  $$H_2(g) \longrightarrow 2H(g) \quad \Delta H = +436 \text{ kJ}$$
  $$2H(g) \longrightarrow H_2(g) \quad \Delta H = -436 \text{ kJ}$$

- Electron gain enthalpy (affinity) is the energy given out when 1 mol of gaseous atoms combine with 1 mol of electrons to form 1 mol of negative gaseous ions.
  (ΔH is always –ve.)
  e.g. electron gain enthalpy of chlorine
  $$Cl(g) + e^- \longrightarrow Cl^-(g) \quad \Delta H = -364 \text{ kJ}$$

Enthalpy of formation of an ionic compound

- The formation of an ionic compound e.g. sodium chloride, involves a series of enthalpy changes best illustrated using a Born Haber cycle.

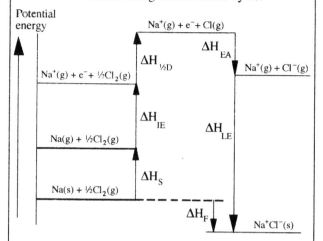

- In the above Born Haber cycle for the enthalpy of formation of NaCl:
  $$\Delta H_F = \Delta H_S + \Delta H_{IE} + \Delta H_{\frac{1}{2}D} + \Delta H_{EA} + \Delta H_{LE}$$
  $$\quad\;\; -ve \quad\; +ve \quad\; +ve \quad\;\; +ve \quad\; -ve \quad\; -ve$$

- Born Haber cycles can be used to find enthalpy changes e.g. lattice-formation enthalpies (the reverse of lattice-breaking enthalpies) and electron gain enthalpies (affinities) which are not obtained experimentally.

Get to know the layout of the cycle really well and appreciate the significance of each step in the cycle!

ΔH_F = enthalpy of formation
$$Na(s) + \tfrac{1}{2}Cl_2(g) \longrightarrow Na^+Cl^-(s) \quad \Delta H = -411 \text{ kJ}$$

ΔH_S = enthalpy of sublimation
$$Na(s) \longrightarrow Na(g) \quad \Delta H = +108 \text{ kJ}$$
(The sublimation stage is essential as first ionisation energy removes electrons from **gaseous atoms**.)

ΔH_{IE} = first ionisation energy
$$Na(g) \longrightarrow Na^+(g) + e^- \quad \Delta H = +500 \text{ kJ}$$

$\Delta H_{\frac{1}{2}D}$ = enthalpy of bond dissociation **(for 0.5 mol)**
$$\tfrac{1}{2}Cl_2(g) \longrightarrow Cl(g) \quad \Delta H = +121 \text{ kJ}$$
$\tfrac{1}{2}$mol   1 mol
molecules   atoms

ΔH_{EA} = electron gain enthalpy (affinity)
$$Cl(g) + e^- \longrightarrow Cl^-(g) \quad \Delta H = -364 \text{ kJ}$$

ΔH_{LE} = lattice-formation enthalpy
$$Na^+(g) + Cl^-(g) \longrightarrow NaCl(s) \quad \Delta H = ?$$

- Only one ΔH term may be calculated from a Born Haber cycle at any time.
  $$\Rightarrow \quad \Delta H_{LE} = \Delta H_F - \Delta H_S - \Delta H_{IE} - \Delta H_{\frac{1}{2}D} - \Delta H_{EA}$$
  $$= -411 - 108 - 500 - 121 - (-364)$$
  $$= -776 \text{ kJ mol}^{-1}$$
  (The large lattice-formation enthalpy compensates for the endothermic processes in the formation of NaCl.)

Atomic particles

- The elements found on our earth have been made from materials once present in stars.

- All elements are composed of atoms.

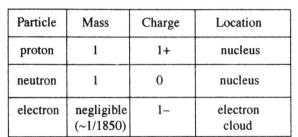

- The three particles which make up almost all atoms have different properties.

Particle	Mass	Charge	Location
proton	1	1+	nucleus
neutron	1	0	nucleus
electron	negligible (~1/1850)	1–	electron cloud

- Isotopes are atoms with the same atomic number but different mass numbers i.e. atoms of the same element with different numbers of neutrons.

Relative atomic mass

- The relative atomic mass of an element is an "average" mass of its atoms taking into account the percentage abundance or fraction of each isotope present.

- Relative atomic mass is calculated from:
  $\sum$(% abundance of each isotope × its mass number)
  or
  $\sum$(fraction of each isotope × its mass number)
  [$\sum$ = "sum of"]

- The relative masses of the isotopes (relative to $^{12}C = 12.000$) and the proportion of each isotope in an element can be found using a mass spectrometer.

- The mass spectrometer "read out" is called a mass spectrum which consists of a series of peaks corresponding to the masses and abundances of each isotope.

> Calculate the relative atomic mass of element X which has three isotopes – ^{27}X, ^{28}X and ^{29}X with % abundances 50%, 36% and 14%, respectively.
>
> Relative atomic mass of X (**not** a real element!)
> = (50/100) × 27 + (36/100) × 28 + (14/100) × 29
> =   13.50   +   10.08   +   4.06
> =   27.64

- The mass spectrum of X would appear as –

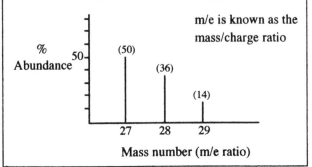

Radioactivity

- Radioactivity is a phenomenon caused by unstable atomic nuclei (radioactive isotopes or radioisotopes) which rearrange to become more stable by the release of particles and/or energy.

- With radioactivity, the release of energy during disintegration is accompanied by emission of alpha- or beta- particles or gamma rays.

- The stability of an atom depends on the relative number of neutrons and protons present i.e. neutrons/protons in its nucleus.

- Lower atomic number, stable nuclei have approximately equal numbers of neutrons and protons i.e. neutron/proton ~1.

- There is an increase in neutron/proton ratio with an increase in atomic number. More neutrons are required to control the repulsions between the increasing number of positively charged protons.

- Unstable nuclei disintegrate until the ratio of neutrons/protons comes within the range of stable nuclei.

The nature and properties of radiation

- There are three types of radiation –

Name	Nature	Symbol	Charge	Mass
alpha (α)	He nucleus	$^{4}_{2}He$	2+	4
beta (β)	electron	$^{0}_{-1}e$	1–	~1/1850
gamma (γ)	electromagnetic radiation	none	none	none

Penetrating power

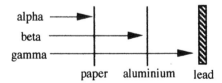

- α particles are absorbed by thin paper; β particles are absorbed by thin aluminium foil and γ radiation is absorbed by a few cms of lead.

The paths of radiation in an electric field

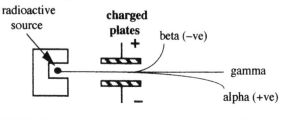

Radioactive (nuclear) reactions

- Nuclear equations show the "parent" nucleus and the decay products formed:
  - (a) the sum of the mass numbers of particles on both sides of the equation must be equal;
  - (b) the sum of the atomic numbers of the particles on both sides of the equation must be equal.

  i.e. for the decay of "parent" isotope X:

  $$_e^a X \longrightarrow {}_f^b Y + {}_g^c Z$$

  $a = b + c$ and $e = f + g$

Loss of an alpha particle $_2^4 He$ or α decay

When a nucleus emits an alpha particle, it loses a helium nucleus which consists of two protons and two neutrons.

The mass number of the "parent" nucleus must decrease by four and the atomic number by two.

Since the atomic number decreases by two units i.e. two protons are lost, the "daughter" nucleus formed is two places lower in the Periodic Table.

e.g. $\quad _{84}^{210} Po \longrightarrow {}_{82}^{206} Pb + {}_2^4 He$

Loss of a beta particle $_{-1}^0 e$ or β decay

Beta particles are high speed electrons which are emitted from the nucleus when neutrons break up into protons and electrons.

i.e.

$$_0^1 n \longrightarrow {}_1^1 p + {}_{-1}^0 e$$

$\quad$ neutron $\qquad$ proton $\qquad$ electron

There is no change in mass number but the atomic number of the "daughter" nucleus is one unit more.

e.g. $\quad _{83}^{212} Bi \longrightarrow {}_{84}^{212} Po + {}_{-1}^0 e$

Gamma radiation or γ decay

Gamma rays are very high energy radiation (short wavelength) from the electromagnetic spectrum and, thus, have no mass or charge.

The emission of gamma radiation has no effect on the mass number or the atomic number of the radioisotope.

- Changing one element into another element is called transmutation.

  e.g. when iron–56 is bombarded with deuterons (hydrogen–2), cobalt–57, an artificial radioisotope is produced.

  $$_{26}^{56} Fe + {}_1^2 H \longrightarrow {}_{27}^{57} Co + {}_0^1 n$$

Artificial (induced) radioisotopes

- Radioactivity can be induced in naturally stable isotopes of elements by bombarding them with neutrons or other high energy particles.

  e.g. $\quad _{13}^{27} Al + {}_0^1 n \longrightarrow {}_{11}^{24} Na + {}_2^4 He$

- The radioactive sodium-24 produced then further decays by beta emission.

  e.g. $\quad _{11}^{24} Na \longrightarrow {}_{12}^{24} Mg + {}_{-1}^0 e$

Half life ($t_{1/2}$) of radioisotopes

- Half life is the time taken for the activity of a radioisotope to decay to half its original value. i.e. the time for half of the radioactive atoms to decay into other nuclei.

- Radioactivity is a random process but because of the very large numbers involved, the decay curves for all radioisotopes have a similar shape.

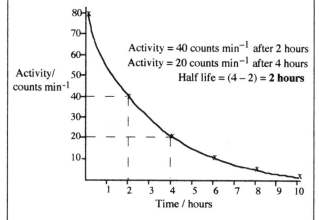

Activity = 40 counts min^{-1} after 2 hours
Activity = 20 counts min^{-1} after 4 hours
Half life = (4 – 2) = **2 hours**

The above decay curve is for a radioisotope with a half life ($t_{1/2}$) of 2 hours.
Do you see that every 2 hours the activity has halved and will read 5 counts min^{-1} after 8 hours have elapsed?

- Although the mass of the original radioisotope halves after each half life period, the total mass of the sample changes only very slightly as a new nucleus forms on decay of each radioactive atom.

- After "n" half lives the fraction of the original isotope (and its activity) left is given by $(1/2)^n$.

- The half life of any radioisotope is independent of the mass of isotope or its chemical state (atom or ion). 1 g samples of the radioisotope element X, the oxide of X and the sulphate of X, all have the same half life but, of course, different initial intensities of radiation since the formula masses differ for these substances.

- Half life is independent of reaction conditions e.g. temperature, concentration, pressure, etc.

Determining half life

- The mass spectrum below was obtained from a 9 day old sample of an α-emitting radioisotope. What is the half life of the radioisotope?

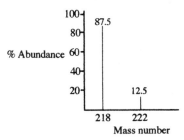

12.5 % of the original α-emitting radioisotope remains, since the decay product (mass no. 218) comprises 87.5%.

% original =>	100%	—> 50%	— 25%	—>12.5%
Fraction => present	1	½	¼	⅛
Half lives => elapsed	–	1	2	3

=> Three half lives have occurred in 9 days.
=> The half life of the radioisotope is 3 days.

Some uses of radioisotopes

- Modern day scientists are finding more and more uses every day for radioisotopes to help "trace events"!

Medical

- Radioisotopes are widely used in the fight against different types of cancers. ^{60}Co, a γ-emitter, is used in irradiation of deep-seated tumours. ^{131}I is taken up by the thyroid gland and can be used to "draw" a picture of the gland or, at greater concentrations, kill cancerous cells. ^{32}P, a β–emitter, is used in the treatment of skin cancer.
Other radioisotope "tracers" e.g. ^{24}Na, are used to follow the flow of blood in the body.

Industrial

- Small samples of short half life radioisotopes can be used to trace fluids (liquids and gases) in pipelines or to detect leaks in water supplies or to test the efficiency of ventilation systems in large buildings.

- Monitoring thickness of production materials.
e.g. ^{90}Sr for tyre cord

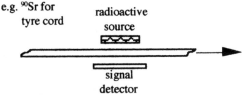

Any change in thickness would alter the detected signal which, when linked to a computer, would change to re-establish correct machine settings.

- Detecting faults in metal castings or welds.

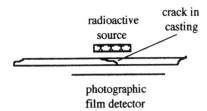

Metal castings and welded components can be examined for any imperfections by employing a radioactive source to "develop" a photographic film.

Scientific research

- Carbon dating is a well used method for determining the age of artefacts from plant or animal origin e.g. the Dead Sea scrolls. There is a fairly constant level of ^{14}C (as CO_2) in the atmosphere and all living plants and animals contain a proportion of this radioisotope of carbon. When organic materials "die", their ^{14}C content begins to decay (by β emission) and from knowledge of the half life of ^{14}C ($t_{\frac{1}{2}}$ ~5700 years) and the proportion of ^{14}C remaining in the sample, the age of the sample can be determined with a reasonable degree of accuracy.

- Watching the uptake and distribution of carbon dioxide by green plants, enabled biochemists to determine the very complex mechanisms involved in the process of photosynthesis. "Labelled" $^{14}CO_2$ molecules were tediously traced throughout various plant structures by the use of special radiation detectors.

- One of the best known radiation detectors is the Geiger–Müller counter where radiation causes the ionisation of gas particles in the detector tube.

Please note that a mass spectrometer is not a radioactivity detector but it, too, can assist chemists in determining some reaction mechanisms with the use of "labelled", but non-radioactive, isotopes in chemical reactions.

e.g. Water removed during the process of esterification has two possible origins:

(i) –OH from the acid and –H from the alkanol;
or (ii) –OH from the alkanol and –H from the acid.

If the alkanol is made using oxygen–18 (indicated by *) and the esterification reaction performed, the water is formed as in (i) above.
Examined in a mass spectrometer, the H_2O has formula mass = 18 (and not 20) which would have been the case if H_2O* had formed.

$$R_1-\overset{*}{O}\underbrace{H \quad H-O}\overset{O}{\overset{\|}{C}}-R_2 \longrightarrow R_1-\overset{*}{O}-\overset{O}{\overset{\|}{C}}-R_2$$
$$\text{alkanol} \qquad \text{acid} \qquad -H_2O \qquad \text{ester}$$

Nuclear fission

- Nuclear fission is the splitting of heavy nuclei such as ^{235}U into two smaller nuclei accompanied by great release of energy. Fission can be induced by energy being given to the nucleus by bombardment with neutrons.

- To produce energy on a large scale, the ^{235}U is bombarded with slow moving neutrons!

$$^{235}_{92}U + {}^{1}_{0}n \longrightarrow {}^{236}_{92}U \longrightarrow {}^{90}_{38}Sr + {}^{144}_{54}Xe + 2{}^{1}_{0}n$$

- This typical fission process is accompanied by the production of two fast moving neutrons which further react with more ^{235}U atoms.

- Two neutrons become four; four become eight; eight become sixteen and very soon a chain reaction is underway! This reaction is controlled by absorbing some neutrons in non-fissionable material in the form of rods e.g. boron.

- The large amounts of energy released are used to generate electricity.

Nuclear fusion

- A nuclear reaction between light atomic nuclei forming a heavier nucleus occurs and a vast quantity of nuclear energy is released.
  e.g. reaction of two deuterium nuclei.

$$^{2}H + {}^{2}H \longrightarrow {}^{3}H + {}^{1}p + Energy$$

$$^{2}H + {}^{2}H \longrightarrow {}^{3}He + {}^{1}n + Energy$$

- Reaction can only take place if the reacting nuclei possess sufficient kinetic energy to overcome the repulsive forces between them. The temperatures associated with fusion reactions e.g. small element to larger element formation in stars, are very high!

- Much research is being undertaken in an attempt to emulate controlled fusion reactions with total safety so that they can be used as a cheaper, limitless supply of energy for future generations.

Background radiation

- A large proportion (~87%) of natural background radiation received by individuals is from cosmic radiation while the rest comes from materials in the Earth's crust.

- Cosmic rays are very high energy radiations falling on Earth from outer space and consist mainly of fragments from heavier nuclei which broke up as they entered the Earth's atmosphere.

- Radon, a naturally occurring radioactive gas, is a decay product of radium. Radon is produced mainly from radioisotopes found in igneous rocks e.g. granites.

- Artificial radiation is mainly medical (~12%).

Nuclear and fossil fuels

- Fuels are sources of energy and include nuclear fuels uranium and plutonium, and the fossil fuels natural gas, oil and coal. The fossil fuels are all valuable sources of chemicals (feedstocks).

- Energy demands are forever increasing and the Earth's reserves of fossil fuels are limited. This has led to a great deal of research to find alternative, efficient sources of energy.

- Both fossil and nuclear fuels give rise to pollutants and are, therefore, "health hazards" to all living things.

- Fossil fuels produce sulphur dioxide and oxides of nitrogen when burned. These gases, when released into the atmosphere, give rise to the problems associated with "acid rain".

- The oxides of carbon released during combustion of fossil fuels – mainly CO_2 – are recognised as main contributors to the atmospheric "greenhouse effect" which will lead to "global warming".

- A major source of pollution which always has devastating effects is large-scale oil spillage.

- Many major accidents occur in coal mining and oil drilling in efforts to search for, and extract, these fuels from the Earth's resources.

- Nuclear energy is a very cheap, limitless supply of energy but nuclear power stations are very expensive to build and to maintain and to operate within strict safety precautions and regulations.

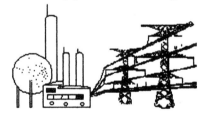

- The public in general seems "scared" of nuclear fuels both from the point of view of reactor safety and storage of nuclear waste. Nuclear fall-out such as happened in the Chernobyl disaster is still fresh in many memories and Sellafield (formerly Windscale) has had many minor scares because of radiation leaks, etc.

- The public, as well as the nuclear industry, is very concerned about "storage" of nuclear waste, especially when it contains radioactive isotopes with very long-lived half lives meaning that the waste will still be very harmful and a threat to the population after several hundred years!

The chemical industry

Your internal assessments and the final examination questions on this topic could ask you to comment on why a particular chemical industry has been developed in a particular area, or you may be asked to think about reasons for siting a brand new chemical plant, or you may be asked to suggest the most appropriate conditions which might have to be used to operate the chemical reactions within the plant.

You may even be asked to comment on the importance of the UK chemical industry (mainly capital rather than labour intensive) and its related manufacturing companies whose marketable goods are the end result of various and often quite complex processing of the chemical materials supplied by the major chemical suppliers.

The large number of companies which make up the UK chemical industry contribute greatly to the national economy of our country and also to the quality of our lives! If you think that the chemical industry has no direct relevance to you, or your lifestyle, take a look at the selection of items below and ask yourself what life would be like if chemists had not been involved in discovering, modifying or processing all the elements, chemical compounds and mixtures utilised in the production of these items!

*In each of the three units of your course, several references to some important industrial processes have already been made. You are, of course, not expected to know all the details of the chemical applications in all branches of chemical industry, but you **are** expected to have an insight into the **general techniques** and **basic principles** employed by such industries.*

Setting up a new chemical plant

"Did you see the look 'Miss' gave me when I told her that she was handing out the wrong notes? I just told her that all that stuff about political, social, historical and economic factors had nothing to do with our chemistry!"

*"You deserved it! If you had just waited a wee while, 'Miss' would have explained why the final outcome in the decision to set up a new industry, or in the choice of operating conditions for any industrial process, must be looked at in light of **all** these things! You need to remember that chemical industries are just businesses trying to make things at a profit for themselves!"*

"Here are some general points for you to keep in mind for your answers to questions dealing with the setting up or the locating of a new chemical plant."

- Do the essential market research, the planned product must be very saleable.

- The planned product must be safe and be able to pass all statutory controls and regulations.

- Find potential customers and estimate the size of the market.

- Is the product likely to be used in the locality?

- Are any/all of the by-products saleable?

- Estimate the profitability from sales.

- Remember that initial layout and production costs will be higher in the early stages until a plant is up and running smoothly.

- Check availability of local authority or government grants to assist location of plant in preferred sites.

- Is site planning permission available or likely to be a problem?

- Check local geography and geology of proposed sites.

- Can construction equipment and personnel be readily brought on to the site?

- Is there an adequate transport and communications network in place for deliveries of raw materials and for deliveries of products to markets?

- Is there adequate/appropriate manpower in the locality?

- Can training facilities be set up readily and at what likely cost?

- People with a wide range of qualifications, skills and experience will work in the chemical plant. In addition to chemical engineers and chemists there will be process operators, technicians, craftsmen, safety personnel, administrators, accountants, secretaries, lawyers, data processors, managers, buyers, sales persons, quality controllers, researchers, instructors, etc.

- If large amounts of fuel are needed, are these available locally or can they be transported or piped to the location?

- If presently reliant on fossil fuels, could the industry adapt at a future date to alternative forms of fuel?

- Is water required for cooling purposes in the plant and is the local water supply suitable and available?

- Is the overall process environmentally "clean"?

- Will local and government regulations on pollution levels be met and maintained?

- Is there solid, liquid or gaseous waste material from the process, and can these be disposed of readily in accordance with local regulations?

- Is there a secondary use for any waste materials?

- Is smoke likely to be a problem in any part of the plant?

- Is there a local ban on the erection of chimney stacks over a certain height?

"I think I'm beginning to see what 'Miss' means!"

Industrial principles

"A few more points from Miss's checklist notes!"

- Whether industries are huge multinational organisations – making a huge range of chemical products – or small, family-owned companies specialising in a single product, they all operate using a similar approach:

  raw materials —> processing —> chemical products
  (initial supplies) (manufacturing stages) (sales and marketing)

- Important raw materials include minerals and ores, fossil fuels, air and water.

- Are the necessary raw materials readily available in the locality of the chemical plant or must they all involve extraction and transportation to site from afar?

- Social and political changes in countries from which some raw materials are obtained may affect supplies and prices and supplies of raw materials, such as fossil fuels, are dwindling in many parts of the world.

- How readily can an industrial plant adapt to likely changes in its supply of raw materials?

- Will extensive treatment of raw materials be needed prior to their use in the manufacturing process?

-  All the preliminary trials at the laboratory stage, to get the best set of conditions of temperature, pressure, etc, for the best yield of product, will have been scaled up and trialled in pilot plant processes. Checks on the development costs are important at all these early stages and the best way to make the product will usually be established in the pilot plant before costly large scale or full production trials get underway. If a problem shows, it's back to the pilot plant for a review of the situation.

- Chemical engineers are responsible for the choice and design of plant machinery to meet the demands of chemical production and for alterations to those components to meet improved production if this is required.

- They will have given serious consideration to the economic costs at each stage in their development work leading to a clear choice between batch production processes or continuous production processes for the main manufacturing stages of the chemical product.

- Remember, the chemical industries are businesses which have grown up to provide the livelihoods for all of its many workers and financial profits for the shareholders who invest heavily in these industries.

- Huge costs in designing, building and trialling production of a chemical product (capital costs) must be met before a product sells on the market.

- Once up-and-running, the plant will have to meet the cost of wages/salaries of company personnel, rent, insurance, electricity and telephone bills, etc, (fixed costs). Such "overheads" are not chargeable to a particular part of the plant or product but must be met no matter how much, or how little, product is made on site.

- The price of raw materials, packaging materials of goods and distribution costs are examples of the expenditure known as variable costs.

So, you can see that a great deal of product selling has to take place before a chemical plant is "in profit" i.e. the production costs (fixed and variable) are exceeded by income from product sales.

- A successful industry always matches its product output to the needs of its customers. The market research division of a successful industry will also be looking ahead for new products for its customers and must be ready to advise its product designers and its research and development teams to "return to the drawing board" in the hope of discovering and developing new products should serious falls in existing product sales result for whatever reason.

- There is no point in having an economically efficient chemical production plant making a product for which there is little, or no, demand!

- Energy costs are great for the largest industries and an efficient energy usage programme must be adopted to keep production costs down!

- Many of the "old industries", where the need for fossil fuel combustion is an unavoidable and an essential part of the plant process, cannot reduce costs readily but seek to utilise the heat generated from any exothermic reactions to either operate and heat the chemical plant or to power other processes in the manufacturing stages.

- For some industries, it is catastrophic to experience regular "shut down" of high temperature stages in a chemical process due to the very high costs involved each time in attaining the high initial starting temperatures required.

A very important industrial process

"Miss was telling me that when she was a pupil at the school, her chemistry teacher told her that you could tell the wealth of a country by the amount of sulphuric acid it used up each year in its chemical industries! It is used to make a lot of fertilisers, paints, pigments, dyes, natural and synthetic fibres, soaps, detergents, and a lot of other chemicals and stuff!"

The Contact Process (H_2SO_4 production)

This process now accounts for almost all the world's production of this extremely important industrial chemical and has sulphur dioxide oxidised to sulphur trioxide over a catalyst in the following equilibrium:

$$2SO_2(g) + O_2(g) \rightleftharpoons 2SO_3(g) \qquad \Delta H \text{ –ve}$$

Raw materials:
Sulphur dioxide, air and water.

Catalyst:
Platinum metal or vanadium(V) oxide, V_2O_5, (some times Na_2O or KOH is present as "catalyst promoter")

Availability:
Air and water (readily available)

Pt catalyst (expensive; easily poisoned by Se or As) - V_2O_5 (pellets; less efficient; but less readily poisoned)

Sulphur dioxide (several sources possible)

(a) burn sulphur in dry air
$$S + O_2 \longrightarrow SO_2$$

(b) by-product from roasting of sulphide minerals
$$FeS_2 + 2O_2 \longrightarrow Fe + 2SO_2$$

(c) from calcium sulphate ('anhydrite') by careful heat treatment with coke, shale, sand and alumina.

The main reaction producing the SO_2 is:
$$2CaSO_4 + C \longrightarrow 2CaO + 2SO_2 + CO_2$$

(d) small amounts found with gas, oil and coal supplies (SO_2 is liquefied for easier handling by cooling and pressurising).

Process conditions:

Temperature
Since the forward reaction is highly exothermic, this is favoured by a lowering of temperature. However, the rate of reaction would be too slow - even with a catalyst present - and so, a compromise temperature of around 450 °C is typical in the reaction chamber.

Pressure
Theoretically, application of high pressure to the equilibrium mixture of gases will increase the yield of SO_2. In practice, atmospheric pressure is used due to the presence of a very high yield (98%) of SO_3!

Removal of the product:

The yield of SO_3 is increased by removing this gas from the equilibrium mixture as it is produced.

The gas is not very soluble in water forming quite dangerous "acid mists" and a number of early plant trials resulted in closures to clear the air!

SO_3 is safely absorbed into 98% sulphuric acid which is thus made even more concentrated producing the very highly concentrated "oleum" or fuming sulphuric acid, $H_2S_2O_7$.

Some of this is removed as one product of the process and some is diluted slightly to be used as absorbent for more SO_3:

$$SO_3(g) + H_2SO_4(l) \longrightarrow H_2S_2O_7(l)$$
$$H_2S_2O_7(l) + H_2O(l) \longrightarrow 2H_2SO_4(l)$$

By allowing a steady trickle of water to be added to the oleum, the 98% concentration of the sulphuric acid product can be maintained.

Energy requirements:

The main reaction on the catalyst surface is highly exothermic and once the catalyst has reached its "working temperature" there is no further need to continue to supply heat to the reaction chamber i.e. the catalyst self-maintains this "working temperature".

Other reactions within the chemical plant are also exothermic and Contact Process plants are designed so efficiently that the excess heat energy from the reaction stages can provide sufficient energy to heat the whole chemical plant and even supply the energy for a number of other processes in the plant.

In some modern "super plants", heat energy, which is excess to requirements, is even sold to neighbouring industries!

This helps to keep the production costs very low and makes the industrial production of sulphuric acid one of the greatest success stories of chemical industry!

The commercial success of the Contact Process worldwide is accompanied by a good environmental image!

The amount of SO_2 released to the atmosphere from the first stage of the process is well below 0.10% and this is negligible compared to the SO_2 output from typical power stations.

Apart from spent vanadium(V) oxide catalyst pellets, there is no solid waste to be disposed!

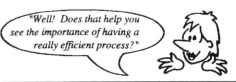

"Well! Does that help you see the importance of having a really efficient process?"